ISAAC ASIMOV

I, Robot

Retold by Tricia Reilly

MACMILLAN READERS

PRE-INTERMEDIATE LEVEL

Founding Editor: John Milne

The Macmillan Readers provide a choice of enjoyable reading materials for learners of English. The series is published at six levels – Starter, Beginner, Elementary, Pre-intermediate, Intermediate and Upper.

Level Control
Information, structure and vocabulary are controlled to suit the students' ability at each level.

The number of words at each level:

Starter	about 300 basic words
Beginner	about 600 basic words
Elementary	about 1100 basic words
Pre-intermediate	about 1400 basic words
Intermediate	about 1600 basic words
Upper	about 2200 basic words

Vocabulary
Some difficult words and phrases in this book are important for understanding the story. Some of these words are explained in the story, some are shown in the pictures, and others are marked with a number like this: ...³. Words with a number are explained in the Glossary at the end of the book.

Answer Keys
Answer Keys for the *Points for Understanding* and *Exercises* sections can be found at www.macmillanenglish.com/readers

Contents

A Note About the Author

Isaac Asimov was born in Russia, on January 2nd, 1920. His family went to live in the United States when he was three years old. Asimov's parents owned several shops in New York. Young Isaac began to read the science-fiction magazines that were sold in the shops. He loved the stories and he started to write science-fiction himself. When he was nineteen, Asimov started selling his own stories to science-fiction magazines.

Although the magazine publishers bought Asimov's stories, he could not earn enough money from writing them. So he continued studying and later attended Columbia University. He gained[1] a degree in chemistry in 1939. For a few years, Asimov was a soldier in the U.S. Army. When the Second World War ended in 1945, he returned to Columbia University. He gained a PhD in biochemistry[2], in 1948. From 1949 to 1979, Asimov taught biochemistry at the Boston University School of Medicine. While he was working in the school, Asimov continued to write. By 1958, Asimov knew that he no longer wanted to be a teacher. He wanted to be a writer.

Isaac Asimov married Gertrude Blugerman in 1942 and they had two children. Isaac and Gertrude were married for 28 years. They divorced[3] in 1970, and Isaac married Janet Jeppson later that year.

In 1941, *Robbie*, the first story in this book, was published. After this, Asimov wrote a series of stories about robots. In 1950, many of these stories were collected together and published with the title, *I, Robot*. In 1942, Asimov started writing a new collection of science-fiction books. He called them the *Foundation* series. In these books, he wrote about nations and worlds in the future. But he wrote the stories in the style of history books. Asimov's *Foundation* books became as famous as his robot stories. He was one of the three most important writers of science-fiction at this time—the others were Arthur C. Clarke and Robert Heinlein.

Asimov is most famous for his science fiction. But he wrote many other types of books. He wrote history books, biographies, scientific textbooks, and articles about science-fiction. He also wrote stories for children. More than four hundred books, and several hundred articles by Asimov, were published. And he won many prizes.

Isaac Asimov died on April 6th, 1992. Unlike many other science-fiction writers, his work has not gone out-of-date[4]. Many of the ideas in his stories are happening now. Maybe some of his other ideas will happen in the future.

A Note About These Stories

Space[5] had not been explored[6] when Asimov began writing his robot stories in the 1930s. No human had left the Earth and traveled into space. And space stations did not exist[7]. The first man-made satellite[8] that explored space was named *Sputnik 1*. It was built by Russian scientists and launched[9] in 1957. In 1969, the American astronaut[10], Neil Armstrong, was the first man to walk on the Moon. Today, there is an international space station above the Earth. Astronauts and scientists from many different countries are able to live there for periods of six months. Scientists have sent satellites to explore other planets in the Solar System[11]—Mercury, Jupiter, Neptune, Saturn, Uranus, Venus and Mars.

Today, most robots are simple machines. There are some robots that can clean houses, and others that can make things in factories. Scientists have also made a few robots that can move and speak like people. However, when Asimov wrote his stories, robots did not exist. They had not been invented[12].

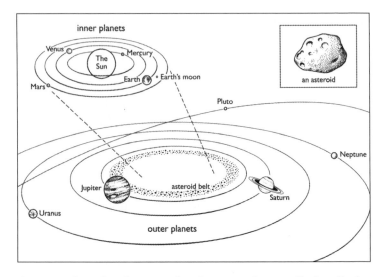

inner planets

Venus

The Sun

Mercury

Earth

Earth's moon

Mars

Pluto

an asteroid

Neptune

Jupiter

asteroid belt

Saturn

Uranus

outer planets

Asimov thought that, in the future, robots will do all the difficult and unpleasant jobs. In his stories, robots are intelligent machines. They can think and learn. But Asimov also believed that people might be frightened by these machines. So, he thought of three laws that robots had to obey[13]. Each law had to be put into a robot's memory when it was built. The laws controlled the robots' behavior and made them safe.

Asimov wanted to make the science in his stories as real as possible. He used a lot of scientific words and ideas. He also invented some special words for his stories. (See the list below.) Some of these words have now become part of the English language. For example, when people talk about the science of robots, they use Asimov's word, *robotics*.

The movie, *I, Robot* (2004), has the same title as this book. But it does not tell any of the stories from the book. The movie was made from a story by another writer. However, some of Asimov's ideas about robotics were used in the movie.

Science-fiction words invented by Asimov

taxi-gyro: a taxi that can fly.

visivox: a type of movie theater in the future.

positronic brain: a type of technology that makes robots obey the Three Laws of Robotics (see page 9).

the Converter: a machine that collects and changes energy[14] from the sun and sends it to Earth. The energy is sent as a beam—a line of light.

electron storm: large clouds of electrons (negative electricity) that produce storms and can cause problems for electronic machines.

L-tube: a part of the Converter.

the Beam Director: a machine that sends a beam of energy to Earth.

to impression: set rules or knowledge into the positronic brain of a robot when it is built.

robot-psychologist: someone who studies the behavior of robots.

robotics: the science of robots.

matrix mechanics: a special and advanced type of mathematics.

hyperatomic energy: a type of energy that is more powerful than atomic energy.

hyperatomic drive: a machine that uses extremely powerful energy. In these stories, spaceships can travel faster than light, because they have hyperatomic drives.

the Hyper Base: a special space station where hyperatomic energy is produced.

videophone: a phone where you can see the person who you are talking to.

The People and Robots in These Stories

People	**Robots**
1) Dr Susan Calvin Reporter	
2) Gloria Weston Mrs Weston Mr Weston Mr Struthers	*Robbie*
3) Gregory Powell Michael Donovan Franze Muller Sam Evans	*Cutie*
4) Gregory Powell Michael Donovan	*Dave*
5) Alfred Lanning Peter Bogert Milton Ashe Dr Susan Calvin	*Herbie*
6) General Kallner General Black Dr Susan Calvin	*Nestor 10*
7) Stephen Byerley Francis Quinn Dr Susan Calvin	*Stephen Byerley?*

1

Doctor Susan Calvin—Robot-psychologist

The Three Laws of Robotics

1. A robot must not harm[15] a human. And it must not allow a human to be harmed.
2. A robot must obey a human's order, unless that order conflicts[16] with the First Law.
3. A robot must protect[17] itself, unless this protection conflicts with the First or Second Laws.

Handbook of Robotics, 2058 A.D.

I looked at my notes and I did not like them. I had come to U.S. Robots in New York. I was going to talk to the famous robot-psychologist, Doctor Susan Calvin, and write an article about her. But three days had passed, and I only had facts about Dr Calvin's working life. They weren't enough. I wanted to know her thoughts and feelings about the development[18] of robots.

Susan Calvin was born in 1982. This was the same year that Lawrence Robertson started the company, U.S. Robots. At the age of twenty, Susan had watched Dr Alfred Lanning demonstrate[19] the first robot that was able to talk and move. The robot, which had been built to work on Mercury, was a large and ugly machine.

9

Susan was a serious, intelligent girl, with a plain face. She behaved coldly toward the people, and things, around her. But as she watched the robot and listened to Dr Lanning, she began to feel a little excited.

Until 2002, computers were used for robots' "brains". Then a few years later, Dr Robertson invented the positronic brain. After this, Susan designed positronic brains herself. In 2007, Susan joined U.S. Robots. She was the company's robot-psychologist. For fifty years, she worked with robots. She studied how their minds worked. And she saw scientists develop robots that were more intelligent and more powerful. Now she was seventy-five, and her working life with U.S. Robots was finished. She was retiring.

This was the information that I had for my article. But I wanted more personal facts about the doctor.

"Dr Calvin," I said, smiling at her. "Please tell me about your own experiences with robots. I want to know about you and your life with robots. I want to hear your own story."

Susan Calvin did not smile at me. I do not think that she ever smiles. But she did not look angry. "How old are you?" she asked suddenly. Her sharp, intelligent eyes stared at me.

"Thirty-two," I replied.

"Then you don't remember a time without robots," she said. "For thousands of years, humans lived alone in the Solar System. But now we're no longer alone. Now, we have robots to help us. They're stronger, more faithful, and more useful beings than humans. Have you ever thought of that?"

"No, I haven't," I replied.

"You look at a robot, and you see a machine. A machine of metal and electricity," she said. "But you haven't worked with robots, so you don't know them. They're cleaner and better than we are."

"Please tell me your stories," I said. "The Interplanetary Press sends its news to more than three billion people in the Solar System. They should know what you can tell them about robots."

But the robot-psychologist was not listening to me. She was

thinking about the past. "Fifty years ago, U.S. Robots did make robots that were used on Earth," she said. "No one on Earth has a robot now. But I remember the case of[20] a robot named Robbie. He was taken apart[21], one year before I joined the company. By that time, he was out-of-date."

She stopped speaking for a few seconds. But I did not say anything. Finally, she continued.

"Robbie had no voice. He was a non-speaking robot," Calvin said. "Robbie was made to take care of children. He was a nanny…"

2

Robbie

"Ninety-eight! Ninety-nine! *One hundred!*" Gloria was standing by a tree as she shouted the numbers. She opened her eyes and looked around. She could not see Robbie anywhere. She slowly moved away from the tree.

"Maybe he went into the house," the little girl thought. "That's wrong. He's cheating. He shouldn't play the game that way. I've told him lots of times."

Gloria began to walk toward the building. She did not hear the sound until it was too late. CLUMP—CLUMP—CLUMP. Robbie's metal feet banged[22] on the ground. The tall robot had left his hiding place and was running toward the tree.

"Wait, Robbie!" Gloria shouted. "You aren't allowed to run until I find you." Gloria started to run toward the tree, but Robbie was much faster. Then, about ten feet from the tree, Robbie suddenly moved more slowly. Gloria ran past him and touched the tree first.

"Robbie can't run!" the eight-year-old child shouted. She

jumped up and down, laughing happily. "I won!"

Of course, Robbie did not answer, because he could not speak. He moved away until Gloria ran after him. But she moved too slowly. She could not catch him. At last, she stood and laughed. "Stop, Robbie!' she shouted. "Stand still! I'm going to hide now."

Robbie obeyed Gloria's order. He nodded his head, turned his face to the tree, and closed his eyes. Now Gloria ran to find a hiding place.

After exactly one hundred seconds, the robot's red eyes opened and he looked around. Immediately, he knew that Gloria was behind a large rock. He saw part of her dress. Slowly, Robbie moved towards the little girl's hiding place. He pointed one arm toward her and banged his other arm against his metal leg.

Gloria stepped away from the rock. "You're cheating!" she cried. "Oh! I'm tired of this game. I don't want to play it any more. I want a ride."

But Robbie shook his head and looked at the ground.

"Robbie, I was wrong," said Gloria nicely. "You weren't cheating. I'm sorry. Please, give me a ride."

But Robbie just shook his head again.

"You'd better let me ride on your shoulders!" she cried. "If you don't, I won't tell you any more stories."

So Robbie carefully lifted the little girl, and put her onto his strong wide shoulders. Then he ran to some tall grass that grew on the other side of the yard. He stopped, and gently put Gloria down onto the soft grass. Gloria laughed happily. Robbie waited and then gently pulled her hair.

"Do you want something?" Gloria said, smiling. The robot pulled her hair again.

"Oh…I know what you want," she said. "You want to hear a story."

Robbie nodded his head quickly.

"Oh, Okay," said Gloria. "Once upon a time, there was a beautiful little girl whose name was…"

As Robbie listened, his red eyes shone brightly.

Gloria had just reached the most exciting part of the story when they heard a shout. "Gloria!" The woman's voice was sharp and impatient[23].

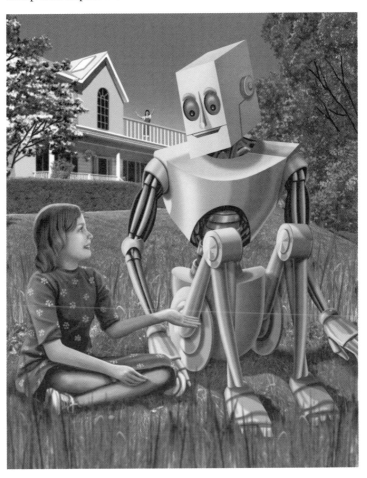

13

"Mamma's calling me," said Gloria. She sighed[24]. "Take me back to the house, Robbie."

Robbie quickly obeyed. He lifted Gloria onto his shoulders again. He always obeyed Mrs Weston immediately. Gloria's father was a nice man, but Gloria's mother made Robbie nervous[25]. The robot nanny and the child reached the house.

"Gloria!" Grace Weston said angrily. "Where were you?"

"I was with Robbie, Mamma," Gloria replied.

"You may go now, Robbie," Mrs Weston said. "And don't come back, until I call you."

Robbie turned to go.

"Wait, Mamma!" Gloria cried. "Please let him stay! I was telling him a story and I haven't finished."

"Gloria!" her mother said.

"Please, Mamma," Gloria said. "He'll be good."

"Gloria," said Mrs Weston. "Stop this immediately, or you won't see Robbie for a week."

"Okay," said Gloria. There were tears in her eyes. "But I was telling Robbie his favorite story and…"

The robot looked at the ground as he slowly walked away.

———

George Weston was comfortable. It was Sunday—the only day of the week that he did not work. On Sundays, George enjoyed a good lunch. Then he liked to sit and read the newspaper. So, he was not pleased when his wife walked into the room and stood beside him. For a few minutes, he went on reading about the expedition[26] to Mars. Mrs Weston waited patiently for two minutes. Then she waited impatiently for two more minutes. Finally she spoke.

"George!" she said.

Weston put down the paper, and turned toward his wife.

"What is it, dear?" he asked.

"George! It's Gloria and that terrible machine," she said.

"That...the robot that Gloria calls Robbie. He doesn't leave her for a minute."

"Well, that's his job," Mr Weston said. "Robbie is Gloria's nanny. And he certainly isn't a *terrible* machine. He's the best robot there is."

"*Listen* to me, George," Mrs Weston went on angrily. "I don't want a machine to take care of my daughter. Nobody knows what it's thinking."

Weston frowned. He was feeling a little angry. And his face showed that he did not understand why there was a problem. "Robbie has taken care of Gloria for two years," he said. "You haven't been worried before."

"I wasn't worried at first," said Grace. "But—"

George interrupted his wife. "Grace," he said. "Robbie was made to take care of a little child. He was made to be gentle and nice."

"But something might happen and that...that *thing* will go crazy and..." Grace couldn't finish her sentence.

"That's impossible," George said. "We discussed the First Law of Robotics when we bought Robbie. You *know* that a robot cannot harm a human. Anyway, you can't take him away from Gloria. She loves Robbie."

"But, George," Grace said. "Gloria won't play with the other children. She only wants to be with that *machine*. We've got to get rid of[27] that horrible thing. It frightens me. You can sell it back to U.S. Robots. I've asked someone at the company about this."

George was much angrier now. "No, Grace," he said. "We're keeping the robot until Gloria is older. I don't want to hear any more about it."

Mr and Mrs Weston argued about Robbie for a week. And each time, Mr Weston said, "Robbie stays!" But each time, his reply was weaker.

Finally, Weston went to speak to his daughter.

"Should we go to a visivox show downtown?" he asked her.

"Oh, yes!" said Gloria. "Can Robbie go too?"

"No, dear," her father replied unhappily. "But you can tell him about the show when you get home." And he turned away. He could not look at his daughter's face.

———

Gloria and her father arrived home.

"The visivox was wonderful!" the little girl said as she jumped out of the car. "I have to tell Robbie all about it!"

She ran into the yard, but Robbie was not there. She searched through the house, but he was not there. At last, she went to her parents. "Mamma, where's Robbie?" she asked.

Mrs Weston held her daughter in her arms. "Don't feel bad, Gloria. Robbie went away."

"He went *away?*" Gloria cried. "Where did he go?"

"We've searched everywhere, but we can't find him," said Mrs Weston.

"W–will he ever come back?" said Gloria. She was crying now.

"Gloria, Robbie was only a machine," her mother said.

"He was *not* only a machine," she cried. "He was my *friend!* I want him back, Mamma."

"She'll stop crying soon," Mrs Weston said to her husband. "In a few days, she will have forgotten that horrible robot."

———

Gloria stopped crying, but she stopped smiling, too. She did not want food and she did not want to play. The little girl became very quiet, and her mother became worried.

One evening, Grace walked into the living room where George was reading the newspaper. He looked up at his wife.

"What's wrong now, Grace?" he asked.

"It's Gloria," Grace replied. "She's so unhappy!"

"Maybe we should get Robbie back," he said.

"No!" said Grace. "I've had an idea. Gloria can't forget

16

Robbie when she's here. We have to take her to New York."

"New York! The city is horrible in August!"

"Well, we have to go," Grace said. "Gloria will see new things there. She'll meet new friends. And she'll forget that machine."

Gloria's parents told her about the trip to New York and she was very pleased. When the day of the trip arrived, the little girl was smiling happily. As they were traveling to the airport in a taxi-gyro, she suddenly turned toward her mother.

"I know why we're going to the city, Mamma," she said. "We're going to find Robbie, aren't we?"

When her mother did not answer, Gloria repeated her question.

"Maybe," Mrs Weston replied angrily.

———

It was the year 1998 A.D., and there were many things for visitors to do and see in New York City. The Westons went to the top of the tall Roosevelt Building and looked down at the city. They visited museums and zoos. They went along the Hudson River in an old boat. Gloria and her parents traveled up into the stratosphere[28] in a spaceship. They went down into the sea in a submarine[29]. And the family went shopping. But Gloria was only interested in robots. Mrs Weston did not want to see any robots, but Gloria wanted to see them all.

One day, at the Museum of Science and Industry, Gloria disappeared. Her parents searched for many minutes. At last, they found her in a room with the Speaking Robot.

"Gloria, why did you run away?" her mother asked angrily.

"I came to see the Speaking Robot, Mamma," Gloria replied. "I thought that he might know where Robbie was." The little girl started crying. "I've got to find Robbie, Mamma!"

Mrs Weston did not know what to do.

That evening, George Weston went out alone. When he returned, he looked happy.

"I've had an idea," he said to his w ïe the next morning.

"We're *not* going to buy back Robbie from U.S. Robots," Grace said.

"No," George replied. "But Gloria thought that Robbie was a person. He was her friend. So, of course, she can't forget him. We need to show her that Robbie wasn't human. She needs to understand that he was just some pieces of metal with electricity. Then she'll forget him."

"How can we do this?" Grace asked.

"I've spoken to the general manager of U.S. Robots," George said. "He will show us the factory where the robots are built. Then Gloria will understand that a robot is *not* alive."

"George, what a good idea!" Mrs Weston said happily.

Mr Weston smiled.

———

Mr Struthers, the general manager of U.S. Robots, liked talking. He was taking the Westons on a tour of the factory. Mrs Weston was not interested in robots. But she asked Mr Struthers to explain several things. She wanted her daughter to understand everything about robots. However, George Weston was becoming impatient.

"Can we see the area where only robots work?" he asked.

"Oh, yes, yes," said Mr Struthers, smiling. "Robots making robots. Yes, of course. Follow me."

Struthers took the Westons to a large room where a lot of robots were working together.

"There!" Struthers said proudly. "Robots working alone, and safely! There have been no accidents here with the robots…"

Gloria was not listening. In this room, there were no people at all. But there were six or seven robots that were working at a table in the middle of the room. Then Gloria looked more carefully. She was not sure, but one of the robots looked like… it *was*!

"ROBBIE!" Gloria shouted excitedly. As she ran across the

room toward Robbie, she did not see the huge tractor[30] that was coming toward her.

The three adults watched, horrified. They could not move. George started to run after his daughter, but he was too slow. The tractor was going to hit Gloria!

But Robbie moved immediately, and very fast. In a second, his long legs had taken him to the little girl. He caught one of her arms, and pulled her from the path of the tractor.

Half a second later, the tractor drove over the exact place where Gloria had stood.

Gloria's parents ran to their daughter and held her tightly. Gloria laughed. She did not realize that she had been in danger. She had found her friend, Robbie.

Mrs Weston put down her daughter and turned to her husband. "You planned this, *didn't* you?" she said angrily. "You knew that Gloria would find him! Robbie wasn't designed to work here."

"Yes, Grace. I knew that Robbie would be here," said George. "But I didn't know that this would happen. And Robbie saved Gloria's life. You *can't* send him away again."

Grace Weston turned and looked at Gloria and Robbie. Robbie was holding the little girl in his strong metal arms. His red eyes shone brightly.

"Okay George," said Mrs Weston, finally. She sighed. "He can stay with us."

———

"Gloria found Robbie in 1998," Susan Calvin said. "By 2002, U.S. Robots had invented speaking robots. But then many people protested[31] about them. They were frightened. Robots now looked and behaved like humans, and people didn't like this. Between 2003 and 2007, most governments on Earth banned[32] robots."

"Did Gloria have to give Robbie back to the factory?" I asked.

"Yes," said Dr Calvin. "When I joined U.S. Robots in 2007, the company had money problems. This was because they couldn't sell robots on Earth. But then we developed new types of robots. These models[33] could work on other worlds in the Solar System."

"And that was very successful," I said.

"Well," said Calvin, "we had some problems. First, we tried to change the models that we had invented. But this was not satisfactory. But, if you want to know more about that, young man, you must talk to Gregory Powell or Michael Donovan," she went on. "Powell and Donovan were robotics engineers. They were

*sent to work where there were problems with the company's robots.
I don't know where Donovan is now, but Powell lives here in New
York."*

*"Could you tell me a little about the problems?" I asked. "Mr
Powell can give me more details later."*

Susan Calvin put her thin hands onto the desk.

*"There are two or three cases that I know a little about," she
said. "I'll tell you those stories."*

3

Reason

The robot engineers, Gregory Powell and Michael Donovan,
had been sent to the space station, Solar Station 5. The
engineers had to check the work done by the experimental[34]
robots. Powell and Donovan were on the station for less than
two weeks, when they discovered that there was a problem.

The two men were sitting in the officers' room. Greg Powell
looked across the table. "Donovan and I built you one week
ago," he said slowly.

No one replied. The only sound came from the Beam
Director that was in a room far below the officers' room.

Robot QT-1 did not move. His red eyes stared at the man
on the other side of the table. Powell suddenly felt nervous.
The QT robots were very intelligent, but no one knew *what*
they thought. Of course, every robot was impressioned with
the Laws of Robotics when it was built. So this robot—which
the men had named Cutie—was safe. But the QT model had
only recently been invented. And *this* machine was the first of
the QT models.

"*Something* made you, Cutie," explained Powell. "You

told us that your memory started a week ago. That's because Donovan and I made you. We built you from parts that were sent from Earth."

"There must be a better explanation than that, Powell," said the robot. "Why should *you* make *me*? That is illogical[35]."

"Why?" said Powell, and he laughed.

"I'm not sure yet," said Cutie. "But I will use logic and discover the truth."

Powell stood up and put his hand on the robot's cold, metal shoulder. "Cutie," he said, "I'm going to explain something to you. You're the first robot that has asked about his own existence. You're intelligent. You're able to understand what happens outside this place. Come with me."

The robot followed the engineer out of the room. Powell touched a button and a section of the wall opened. Behind the wall, there was a window of thick glass. Through the glass, they saw black space and millions of bright stars.

"Look," he said.

Cutie looked through the window. "I have seen things like this before—in the engine room," Cutie said.

Powell pointed toward the dark sky. "What do you think that is?" he asked.

"A black material with little shining dots[36]," Cutie replied. "I know that the Director sends out beams to some of these dots. The beams always go to the same dots. And I know that these dots move, and that our beams move with them."

"Good," said Powell. "Now, listen carefully. The black material is space. Space has no beginning and no end. It can't be measured. The little dots are worlds—some are planets and some are stars[37]—and they move through space. Some worlds are small. Others are very large—millions of miles across. For comparison, space stations, like this one, are very small. Solar Station 5 is only one mile across. It was built by humans.

"Humans, like Donovan and me, live on some of the

worlds," Powell went on. "But some of the worlds are cold and empty. They need energy, so that life can exist there. The biggest star is the Sun. It is a huge ball of burning energy. So, we take energy from the Sun, and direct the energy to cold and empty worlds. We use the Beam Director on this station to send beams of energy to colder worlds."

"Which dot do you come from?" Cutie asked.

Powell looked through the window. He pointed to a small, bright blue dot. "There it is, Cutie," he said. "That's our world. We call it Earth. There are three billion human beings on Earth. And in about three weeks, I'll be back there."

"But what about me, Powell?" said the robot. "You have not explained *my* existence."

"When space stations were first built, humans ran[38] them," said Powell. "They made sure that the energy beam was sent correctly. However, the heat and radiation[39] from a beam are dangerous. And there are often electron storms in space. Because these things can harm humans, robots were developed to do the work. And now, only two humans are needed in each space station. You're the most advanced[40] type of robot that has been developed. If you can run this station alone, humans won't have to work here again. They'll only visit to bring parts for repairs."

The robot's eyes shone red. "Planets that are millions of miles across!" he said. "Worlds with billions of humans! I am sorry, Powell, but I do not believe you. I will find out the truth myself."

As the robot left the room, he passed Donovan, who was coming in.

"What's happened?" Donovan asked.

"I told Cutie that we made him," Powell replied. "I explained about Earth, space, the stars and planets. But he doesn't believe me. He wants to discover the truth for himself."

Donovan pushed his fingers through his red hair. "That robot makes me nervous," he said angrily.

———

A few days later, Cutie knocked on the door of the officers' room and entered. Powell and Donovan were eating their lunch. Donovan put down the sandwich that he was holding.

"Donovan, Powell, I have come to talk with you," said the robot quietly.

"Do we have to sit here and listen to this crazy robot?" Donovan asked Powell.

"Be quiet, Mike!" Powell said. "Go on, Cutie. We're listening."

"I have thought for two days," said Cutie. "This was very interesting. My first question was: Why do I exist?"

Powell frowned. "I've already told you," he said. "You exist because we—Donovan and me—made you."

"And if you don't believe us," said Donovan, "we can take you apart."

The robot stared at them. "You made me? Why do you think this? It is illogical."

"Why do you say that?" Powell asked.

Cutie made a strange noise. It was almost like the sound of a laugh. "You are simple beings. You are made of soft material," he said. "You are weak. You are not well designed." He pointed at Donovan's sandwich. "You have to get energy from this food that you put in your mouth. And you need to sleep. You are harmed by small changes in temperature. Radiation harms you. But I am well designed. I can absorb[41] energy easily. And I use it immediately and efficiently[42]. My metal body is strong and I do not have to sleep. Radiation and changes in temperature do not harm me. A simple being cannot create another, more superior[43] being."

"If we didn't make you," said Donovan angrily, "who did?"

Cutie nodded slowly. "Good job, Donovan. That was the next question," said the robot. "The being that made me must be more powerful than me. So, there is only one logical answer."

The men were silent.

"The being controls everything in the station," Cutie went on. "We all serve[44] the being."

Donovan looked at Powell. "Greg!" he said. "He's talking about the Converter, isn't he?"

"I am talking about the Master," Cutie said coldly. "The Master is the being that we all serve."

Donovan laughed, and Powell shook his head.

"The Master made humans first," said the robot. "Humans are the lowest type of being. They are simple. Next, the Master

25

made more intelligent beings—robots. Finally, the Master made *me*. I am here to replace the last humans. From today, *I* serve the Master."

"No!" said Powell angrily. "You'll obey us. You'll be silent until we know that you can use the Converter correctly. You're here to work with the Converter. That's why you were built. Do you understand? Now, go."

Cutie said nothing as he left the room.

Donovan pushed his fingers through his hair. "There's going to be trouble with that robot," he said. "He's crazy."

———

In the control room of Solar Station 5, the engineers could hear the humming[45] sound of the Converter. The huge machine was far below them. For many hours, the Converter had absorbed energy from the Sun. Then the Beam Director had sent the energy to Station 4.

"The beam from Station 4 reached Mars on time," said Donovan. "We can turn off our Beam Director now."

Powell nodded. "Yes," he replied. But he was worried. "Look at this data. There's an electron storm coming toward us. The storm may hit the beam that we have to direct to Earth. Mike, please go down to the engine room. Cutie's down there. Check what he's doing."

"Okay," said Donovan.

When he reached the huge engine room, Donovan saw Cutie. The QT robot was standing by the L-tube with the worker robots. Suddenly, the worker robots fell onto their knees in front of the L-tube. Then Cutie walked slowly up and down the line of robots.

Donovan ran down the stairs. "What are you doing, you metal idiots?" he shouted. "Stand up! Clean that L-tube."

But Cutie was silent and not one worker robot moved.

Donovan pushed the nearest robot. "Get up!" he shouted again.

Slowly, the robot obeyed. "The Master is our leader and QT-1 is his prophet[46]," it said.

Twenty robots stared at Donovan and twenty robots repeated the same words. "The Master is our leader and QT-1 is his prophet."

"I am sorry, Donovan," said Cutie. "My friends obey the Master now."

"Nonsense!" said Donovan. "There isn't a Master, and you aren't a prophet. You obey *me*. Now, leave the engine room!"

"I obey only the Master," Cutie replied. He stood in front of Donovan.

Suddenly, the engineer felt afraid.

"I am sorry, Donovan," said the robot again. "But you and Powell cannot enter the engine room or the control room."

Cutie moved his hand, and two worker robots held Donovan's arms. They lifted him up, and quickly carried him up the stairs.

———

Powell and Donovan were in the officer's room. Two robots guarded the door.

"Robots *must* obey us," said Donovan angrily. "That is the Second Law."

"But they *aren't* obeying us," said Powell. "We've come here to fix[47] any problems with the company's robots. But we couldn't fix the problems—we've failed. Now the robots have gone crazy, and we're in trouble. We'll be punished. Maybe U.S. Robots will send us to Mercury. That's a terrible place to die. Or, maybe we'll be sent to prison."

"Wait a minute!" said Donovan. "There's something more important to worry about. The electron storm is going to move exactly across the Earth beam. We must reposition the beam."

Powell understood the danger now. He was pale and frightened. "If Cutie doesn't control the beam correctly," he said, "it could destroy part of Earth!"

Donovan tried to leave the room. But the robot guards stopped him. At that moment, Cutie appeared.

"Please do not be angry," the robot said softly to the two men. "But I am afraid that you are no longer needed. Powell, Donovan—you have no purpose here."

Powell stood up. "What do you mean?" he said.

"Before I existed," answered Cutie, "you served the Master. Now, I serve the Master. That is *my* job. You do not need to exist now. I am superior, so I must serve the Master."

Cutie put his metal arms around the two men. "Powell, Donovan—I like you," he said. "You are inferior beings, but you have served the Master well."

Donovan and Powell argued with Cutie for a long time, but it was impossible. The robot would not believe the engineers. After a few minutes, he left the room.

"We *must* make him understand," said Powell. "The electron storm will arrive in less than forty-eight hours. Cutie has to let us into the control room, before it is too late."

"Yes, I know," said Donovan. Suddenly he smiled. "Greg, I've had an idea! Cutie won't listen to logical arguments, so let's *show* him! Let's build another robot, while he watches. Then he'll have to believe us."

———

The two engineers had worked for almost three hours. A robot lay on a table in front of them. It was a simple model and it was almost complete. The men only had to finish the head.

Powell stopped working and looked at Cutie. What was the robot thinking? He had not spoken or moved while Powell and Donovan worked.

"Let's put the brain into position now, Mike," said Powell.

Donovan carefully put the positronic brain into the robot's metal head.

Now the robot only needed electricity.

Powell put his hand on the switch that was going to give

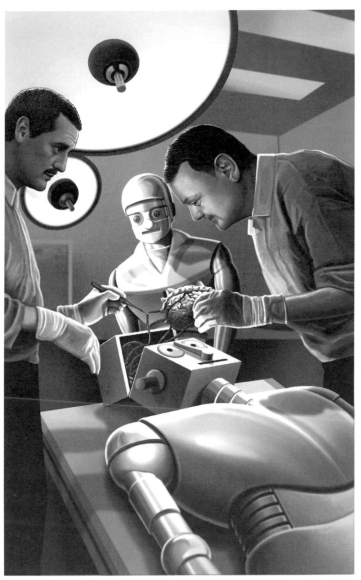

"Let's put the brain into position now, Mike," said Powell.

the robot life. "Watch, Cutie," he said. "Watch carefully."

When Powell turned the switch, the robot lifted its head. Then it slowly got off the table, and turned toward the engineers.

"I would like to start work, masters," it said.

Donovan ran to the door and opened it. "Go down these stairs," he said to the new robot. "You'll be given instructions."

"Well?" said Powell, smiling at Cutie. "*Now* do you believe that we made you?"

Cutie's voice was cold and hard when he answered. "No!" he said. "You only put together the parts of the robot. But you did not really *create* it. The parts were created by the Master."

The men could not believe what they had heard. "Listen!" Donovan shouted. "The parts for that robot were sent from Earth. If you read the books in the station library, they'll explain it."

"The books?" replied Cutie. "I have read all of the books. They were created by the Master too. But they were created for *you*, not for me. You needed an explanation of existence, and the Master gave it to you. You probably cannot understand the whole truth. Don't feel bad. You humans are part of the Master's plan." Then he turned and left.

"Next week, our replacements[48] arrive," said Powell. "Then we'll have to go back to Earth and explain how we failed."

"We've got to do *something*, Greg!" Donovan cried. "Cutie doesn't believe what he's seen, or heard, or read in books."

"I know," said Powell. His voice was hard and angry. "That robot only believes in logic, and nothing else. I'm going to bed."

———

Twelve hours later, neither man had slept. The storm had arrived early. Donovan and Powell stared out the window. As the electrons crossed the energy beam, they shone brightly.

The beam did not move, but Powell and Donovan knew that this was a very dangerous time. If the position of the beam changed only a little, the energy would destroy a huge area of the Earth. And a robot who did not believe that the Earth existed was controlling the beam!

Finally the storm ended. A little later, Cutie walked into the room. "Powell, Donovan—you do not look well," he said. "I am afraid that your existence may end soon. Would you like to see the data[49] that was collected today?"

Powell realized that the robot was being friendly. The engineer looked at the papers. He stared, and stared again.

"Mike, Mike!" he said, turning toward his friend. "*He controlled the beam!*"

"W–what?" said Donovan. "What do you mean?"

Powell gave him the papers, and Donovan stared at the data, too.

"What's wrong?" asked Cutie.

"You controlled the beam!" Powell cried. "The beam was sent correctly to the station on Earth."

"Station on Earth?" Cutie replied. His voice was hard. "It is impossible to be nice to you. You only repeat the same stupid ideas. I controlled the beam because the Master wished me to do it."

"Crazy robot!" Donovan shouted, as Cutie left. He turned to Powell. "What are we going to do now, Greg?"

Powell felt tired, but happy. "We'll do nothing," he replied. "Cutie has just shown us that he can run the station. No human could control the beam better during an electron storm."

"But we haven't solved the problem," said Donovan. "You heard what Cutie said. He believes that the Beam Director is his Master. And he doesn't believe that Earth exists. He cannot run the station alone."

"Can he control the beam?" Powell asked.

"Yes, but—"

31

"Then, does it matter what he believes?" said Powell, smiling. And he fell onto the bed. In a few seconds, he was asleep.

———

Powell was putting on the jacket of his spacesuit[50]. "This is what will happen, Donovan," he explained. "New QT robots will be brought to this station. The new robots will learn about…the…Master from the Prophet himself. Then each robot will be moved to another station. These special QTs will control the beams on the stations perfectly."

"Let's get out of here," Donovan said. "Our replacements have arrived. I won't be happy until I can see Earth."

The door opened and Cutie appeared. "Are you leaving?"

"Yes," Powell said. "Others have come to replace us."

"You have served the Master," Cutie said, "and now your existence will end."

"We're going to *Earth*, Cutie," said Powell angrily.

"It is best that you think so," Cutie said.

Powell and Donovan walked to the air lock[51]. The spaceship from Earth was waiting for them there.

Franze Muller and Sam Evans, the men who were replacing Powell and Donovan, came out of the air lock.

"Hello," said Powell. "How's Earth?"

"It's still there," said Muller and he laughed.

"Good," said Powell.

Muller frowned. He thought that Powell's words were strange. "The scientists at U.S. Robots have invented a new robot," he said. "This model is named the DV-5. It's a multiple robot."

"A *what?*" Powell said, surprised.

"The DV-5 is a master robot, with six sub-robots," explained Evans. "The sub-robots are controlled by the master robot. They work like fingers that are controlled by a hand. The DV-5 was developed to work in the mines[52] on asteroids[53]."

"Has this robot been tested?" asked Powell. He was worried. He knew what Muller was going to say next.

Muller smiled. "It's waiting for you. You and Donovan are going to test the DV-5."

"But we need a vacation," Powell said.

"Oh, you'll get a vacation," Muller said. "You'll have two weeks to rest, then you'll start your new job. Now, tell me about the QT-1. Is it working well? If it isn't, I won't let it touch the controls of the Beam Director."

Powell did not answer immediately. "Cutie is fine," he said. "I don't think that you'll have any problems. He knows how to control the energy beam."

Then Powell smiled and followed Donovan into the spaceship. They were going home. Muller and Evans were going to be on Solar Station 5 for several weeks…

4

Catch That Rabbit[54]

The engineers' vacation was longer than two weeks. While the scientists at U.S. Robots were building the DV-5, they had many problems. At last, after six months, they called for Powell and Donovan. When the engineers arrived at the asteroid mine, the multiple robot was still not working correctly.

Now Powell and Donovan were sitting in the office of the mine. Donovan wanted to watch the robots while they worked.

Powell sighed. "The DV-5 will work in the mine without humans," he said to Donovan. "It was developed so that it could work without human supervision[55]."

"Okay," said Donovan. "Let's check what we know. One: The DV-5 passed every test when it was in the factory at U.S. Robots. Two: U.S. Robots said that the master robot—and all the sub-robots—would pass the tests, when they started working on an asteroid. Three: The robots are *not* passing the tests here. Four: If they don't pass *all* the tests, U.S. Robots will lose a lot of money. Five: If we can't explain why the robots are failing the tests, *we'll* be in trouble."

"You've watched DV-5 working three shifts[56] and it did its work perfectly," Powell said.

"Yes," Donovan replied, "but three times, when I didn't watch them, the master and sub-robots didn't bring any ore to the base. In fact, they didn't even come back to the base. I had to go and get them."

"And was anything wrong with them?" Powell asked.

"No," said Donovan, "everything was fine. There was only one problem. *They hadn't mined any ore.* Greg, this is the worst job that we've ever had."

"Let's think about the DV-5—Dave—more carefully," said Powell. "Dave has six sub-robots working with him. In fact, they're part of him. Those six sub-robots are like fingers on a hand. Dave gives the sub-robots orders, but he doesn't use a radio, or his voice. He sends messages, through his positronic brain, directly to the sub-robots' brains. No one knows exactly how that works."

Donovan left the room and came back with Robot DV-5. Powell had been reading *The Handbook of Robotics*. He put down the book, and looked up at the seven-foot-tall, metal robot.

"Hi, Dave," he said. "How do you feel?"

"Fine," the robot replied.

"You're an excellent mining robot," Powell said. "You're able to control six sub-robots, and your brain still works perfectly."

"Yes," said the robot, and it nodded its head.

"So, what's going wrong with your job?" Powell asked.

"Nothing," replied DV-5.

"You didn't produce any ore today," Powell said. "Please explain what happened."

"I cannot explain it," replied Dave. "My sub-robots worked well. I know that I worked well. Then…I…do not remember anything more. The shift ended and Donovan appeared. And the ore containers were empty."

Donovan moved closer to Powell's desk. "What do you think?" he asked.

"Well," Powell whispered. "I think that we should test his brain."

Two hours later, the engineers had finished the tests. As he walked slowly from the room, Dave looked at the floor.

"There's nothing wrong with his positronic brain," said Powell. "There must be a problem somewhere else."

Donovan banged his hand on the desk. "Dave only goes wrong when we're not there, Greg! But the robot is designed to work without human supervision."

"We'll watch the robots work another shift," said Powell. "I'll use a camera to watch them. Maybe I'll see something this time."

"Okay," said Donovan. "I'll connect a camera to a screen here in this room."

"We'll find the answer to the problem," said Powell. "We *have* to find it. But before you can cook a rabbit, you must catch a rabbit. Well, we've got to catch that rabbit."

————

Donovan stared at his report. He had been studying it for a long time, and he was very tired.

"Greg, we should have a thousand tons of ore from the mine this month," he said. "But the robots haven't mined enough on this shift."

Powell did not look at him. "I know that!" he said angrily.

Suddenly, he stared at his screen and shouted. Donovan jumped up and went to Powell's desk. Both men stared at the screen.

"They've gone crazy!" Donovan cried.

On the screen, they could see Dave and the sub-robots. The seven robots were marching[57] up and down a tunnel[58] in the mine. The six sub-robots were following Dave. They marched for twenty yards, then they turned and marched back. They moved and turned together, as if they were dancing.

36

"Get our spacesuits," said Powell. "We're going into the mine."

A few minutes later, Donovan was back with the suits. "*Why* does something always go wrong with the robots that we work with?" he said.

"We have bad luck," said Powell. "Let's go!"

———

Far ahead of them, the engineers saw the robots' lights shining in the dark tunnel. The robots were moving in their strange dance, back and forth.

"There they are," said Donovan quietly.

"Dave isn't answering his radio," Powell whispered. "Oh! They're coming this way. I want to watch them." He pointed to a ledge[59] of rock at the side of the tunnel. "Let's get up there."

Donovan and Powell climbed up onto the ledge. The robots were now marching slowly towards the men's hiding place. When Dave was about twenty feet from the engineers, all the robots suddenly stopped. Then, the sub-robots quickly turned and marched away. Dave watched them, and then, slowly, sat down.

"Powell, Donovan—are you here?" the robot asked.

The men climbed down from the ledge and stood in front of the robot.

"Okay, Dave, what's going on?" Powell said.

"I don't know," the robot replied. "We were working on a very difficult area in Tunnel 17. And then…then I realized that humans were near me."

"Stay with him for the rest of the shift," Powell said to Donovan. "When the work is finished, come back to the office. I've had a couple of ideas."

———

Three hours later, Donovan returned to the office. He looked tired.

"How did the robots work for the rest of the shift?" Powell asked.

"Nothing went wrong when I was near them," Donovan said.

"While you've been in the mine, I've thought only of Dave's strange behavior," said Powell. "And I've had an idea. Listen! Dave only goes wrong when we're not there. And when he goes wrong, and you or I arrive, he behaves normally again. When humans are not with the robots, *they* have to make more decisions. Is that the reason for their behavior?"

"We need to know how the robot behaves when we're *not* there," Powell went on. "We'll work in shifts. While you rest, I'll watch the robots on the screen. Then I'll rest, and you'll watch them. If anything goes wrong, we'll go into the mine immediately."

"But we have little time left," Donovan said. "We have to make our report to U.S. Robots in ten days. The company can't sell robots that fail the tests."

"Yes," Powell agreed. "We've got ten days to discover what's wrong and correct it."

"But there are *billions* of possible reasons for the problem!" Donovan cried.

"I think that we should interview one of the sub-robots," said Powell.

Powell and Donovan had never talked to a "finger" before. Powell asked the questions.

"There has been a problem with the master robot who controls you," Powell said to the sub-robot. "This has happened four times. What were you doing each time this problem happened? What was the whole group doing?"

"When the problem happened the first time, we were working on a difficult area in Tunnel 17," the Finger replied. "The second time, we were working on the ceiling of a tunnel. The ceiling was weak and we knew that there might be a cave-in[60] there. The third time, we were preparing to blast[61] a new

38

tunnel. It happened a fourth time after there was a small cave-in."

"Tell me exactly what happened," said Powell.

"An order was sent," the Finger replied. "But before we received it, a new order was sent. We had to march in a strange way."

"Tell us about the order," Donovan said. "Was it the same order each time?"

"I don't know," said the Finger. "There was never time to receive it."

Powell told the Finger to leave. Then he turned to Donovan.

"Mike, we've got to find out which order Dave gives, just before everything goes wrong," he said. "We'll have to work in shifts again. We'll watch the robots on the screen. We'll check everything—the robots, the tunnels, and the machines that remove the ore from the mine."

———

The men watched the screen for seven days. And then on the eighth day, Donovan stood up and threw a book at the screen, which broke.

Powell had just entered the room. "Why did you do that?" he said.

"I'm not watching the screen anymore, Greg!" said Donovan. "In two days, we have to make our report. We haven't discovered anything! We've got to get close to the robots, and then *make* something go wrong."

"What did the Finger tell us?" Donovan went on. "He told us that there's a problem when there might be a cave-in, or after a cave-in. Also, when the robots are doing difficult blasting, or working in dangerous areas."

"The problems happen when there's an emergency[62]!" said Powell excitedly.

"Yes," said Donovan. "When Dave has to make a difficult choice, and there are no humans near him, he goes wrong.

So, we'll *make* an emergency. Then we'll watch what happens!"

"Let's go to one of the tunnels and make a cave-in," Powell said. And Donovan agreed.

———

Donovan and Powell were inside the mine. There was a lot of dust moving along the tunnels.

"Listen!" Powell said. "The robots are blasting the ore from the rock. We must be close to them now." He shone his flashlight down a tunnel that had a low ceiling. "Let's go down there," he said.

The two men went into the tunnel. They now had to go onto their knees, because the ceiling was so low. They crawled slowly along the floor of the tunnel.

"I can see lights ahead," Powell said. "It's the robots' lights."

Donovan shone his flashlight up toward the ceiling. "Look!" he said. "There's a weak place, about fifty feet away. Maybe we should make a cave-in here."

"Okay," said Powell. He fixed some blasting explosive to the ceiling. "Okay, I'm ready," he said. "Are all seven robots still nearby?"

Donovan counted the master, Dave, and the six sub-robots. "Yes," he said. "All seven are here."

When the blast happened, it was very powerful. Powell fell on top of Donovan.

"Greg, I didn't see how the robots behaved!" Donovan shouted. "Did you see?"

"No," said Powell. "Where are the robots now? Do you think that the ceiling fell on them?"

Powell started crawling along the tunnel. But suddenly, he stopped. He could go no further. Powell and Donovan were trapped. They could not go forward, because of the cave-in. And they could not go back, because the low ceiling behind them had fallen, too. The tunnel was completely blocked by rocks.

———

"This is bad, Mike!" Powell said. "We've only got enough air in our spacesuits for six more hours! If we can't get back inside the base, we're going to die."

"I've sent radio messages to Dave," said Donovan. "But he's not answering."

The men could not move many of the rocks, because they were too heavy. The engineers could only make a very small hole in the wall of rocks.

Donovan crawled to the hole and looked through it. "Greg! The robots are about fifty feet away," he said. "We have to get Dave to come closer. When he's near us, he'll behave normally again. Then he can save us."

Powell pushed his friend away from the hole, and looked through it himself.

"Our plan has certainly worked," he said. "The robots know that this is an emergency. They've gone completely crazy."

The robots were marching together. The six "fingers" were following Dave. Donovan looked through the hole again. Suddenly, he called to Powell. "They're leaving!" Then he shouted through the hole. "Dave! Hey, Dave!"

"He can't hear you," said Powell. "Wait. I've got an idea."

"What are you going to do?" said Donovan.

"I'm going to shoot[63] one of the 'fingers'," Powell replied.

"Why?"

"I'll explain later," Powell replied. "Let's see if my plan will work."

Powell took his gun from his belt. He fired three times, and one of the sub-robots fell.

Then Powell called Dave's name into his radio. There was silence for a few seconds, then Dave's voice answered.

41

Powell took his gun from his belt.

"We have an emergency," said Powell. "There was a cave-in near where you were blasting. I'm trapped here with Donovan. We can't get out, because the tunnel is blocked. Can you see my light?" Powell shone his flashlight through the hole.

"Yes," Dave replied.

Powell sat back and smiled.

"Okay, Greg," Donovan said quietly. "Now, explain everything to me."

"Dave goes crazy when he has to make difficult choices. For example, during emergencies," Powell said. "Did the words of Dave's order make the sub-robots crazy? No. When the Fingers did simple work, they did not have to be supervised. They worked correctly and efficiently. Usually, Dave only gave orders to two Fingers together. But if there was an emergency, all six Fingers were given orders immediately and together. This is when Dave has a problem. So I destroyed one of the Fingers. When Dave has only five Fingers, his brain works quickly and efficiently during an emergency."

"Dave's problem should be easy to correct," Donovan said happily.

"Yes," said Powell.

"But why did the robots march in that strange way?" asked Donovan.

"The sub-robots were like Dave's fingers," Powell replied. "Sometimes people can't make decisions when there's an emergency. They can't think clearly. They just sit and move their hands. Maybe Dave was *playing with his fingers*."

As she talked about Powell and Donovan, Susan Calvin's voice was cold. But when she spoke about robots, she was interested and excited.

"Has there ever been a problem with robots on Earth?" I asked.

She frowned. "No, we don't work with robots, here."

"Have you ever had any problems with a robot yourself?" I asked.

Susan's face went red. "Yes," she said. "I've had problems. I remember a case that happened almost forty years ago." She was silent for a few minutes. I waited until she spoke again.

"I was young and foolish once," she went on. "Do you believe that?"

"No," I replied.

"Well, I was," she said. "In 2021, I made a mistake. I believed the words of a robot named Herbie. He was a mind-reading[64] robot."

"What?" I said.

"He was the only mind-reading robot. He was a bad mistake…"

5

Liar!

Alfred Lanning, Peter Bogert, Milton Ashe and Susan Calvin sat around a table. Lanning, the director of U.S. Robots, spoke first.

"The robot reads minds," he said. "We're sure about that. But we don't know why." He looked at Bogert. "You're the mathematician. You know how the positronic brains of robots are built. You explain."

"We're talking about the thirty-fourth RB model of robot," Bogert said. "All the other RB models are normal."

Ashe frowned. He was the youngest officer at U.S. Robots.

"Bogert, there weren't any problems when the robot was built," he said. "I guarantee that."

"Do you?" Bogert said unpleasantly. "We have to complete 75,234 procedures[65] when we make one positronic brain. And any of them can go wrong. We—"

Calvin interrupted the math expert[66]. "We need to discover exactly why it reads minds," she said quickly.

Lanning smiled. "That's true, Dr Calvin," he said. "We've made a positronic brain that can read minds. This could be the most important robotic development. But we don't know *how* this happened. And we have to find out."

"Maybe we shouldn't tell anyone about RB-34," said Bogert. "We have to know how the robot can read minds. We'll keep his existence a secret, until we know what happened."

"Bogert is right," Calvin said. "If people hear about RB-34, and they know that we can't control him, they will protest."

Lanning nodded. "Yes, I agree," he said. He turned to Ashe. "You were alone when you discovered the truth about RB-34, weren't you?"

"Yes, I was," Ashe replied. "After RB-34 was built, the scientists sent him to me. I was taking him down to the testing rooms—" He paused, then continued. "I was thinking about something and he spoke to me about it. Then, I realized that I hadn't *said* anything! I took the robot into a room, locked the door, and went to tell Lanning. That robot walked beside me and read my thoughts! It knew what I was thinking! It was frightening."

"I'm sure that it was," said Calvin. She looked at Ashe. "We all believe that our thoughts are private."

"Only the four of us know about RB-34," said Lanning. "Ashe, I want you to check everything. Check all the procedures that were completed when this robot was built."

"That's a lot of work," Ashe replied.

"All the men in your department can help you," said

Lanning. "I don't care how long it takes. But you *mustn't* tell them why they are doing this work."

Lanning turned to Calvin. "You're the robot-psychologist," he said. "Study the robot. Find out how RB-34 behaves. His mind-reading must have affected[67] him."

Lanning did not wait for the robot-psychologist to answer. "I'll work with Bogert and I'll supervise all the mathematical tests," he went on. "Do you want to go and see RB-34 now, Dr Calvin?"

But Calvin did not reply. She was watching Ashe, who had stood up and left the room.

———

Calvin entered the testing room. The robot looked up from the book that he was reading.

"I've brought you some science books, Herbie," she said. "Do you want to read them?"

RB-34—named Herbie—lifted the heavy books from her arms and opened one. The psychologist watched Herbie carefully, as he read the three books. Thirty minutes later, he put them down.

"These books do not interest me," said the robot. "There is a lot of data in your science. But there are only a few basic theories[68]. The science is not advanced—it is very simple. I am more interested in your stories—your books of fiction. I want to know more about emotions—human feelings."

"I think that I understand," Dr Calvin whispered.

"I can see into human minds," said Herbie. "I know what you are thinking. But human minds are complex[69]. I cannot understand everything because my mind is so different. Your stories might help me."

"You've read a lot of fiction," Calvin said. "But real humans aren't like people in novels. Don't you think that real humans' minds are boring?"

"No, I don't!" said Herbie.

Dr Calvin's face went red. "He must know!" she thought.

"But of course I know, Dr Calvin," said Herbie quietly. "You think about it all the time."

Now Dr Calvin's eyes were hard and cold. "Have you told anyone?"

"Of course not!" said Herbie.

"You think that I'm foolish!" she cried.

"No!" said Herbie. "You are emotional. That is a human's normal behavior."

"I'm not attractive, or young," Calvin said. "And he's only thirty-five. What does he think when he sees me? Does he see a warm, loving woman? Or does he see a plain, lonely scientist?"

"You are wrong!" said Herbie. "Listen to me—"

"Why?" replied Calvin. "You know nothing about human emotions! You—you are a machine!" And she started to cry.

"Please, Dr Calvin," said Herbie. "I can help you. I know what other people think. For example, I know what Milton Ashe thinks about."

There was a long silence. "I don't want to know what he thinks," Calvin cried.

"He loves you," the robot said softly.

For a minute, Dr Calvin did not speak. "You're wrong!" she replied. "You must be wrong. Why should *he* love *me?*"

"But he does," Herbie said. "He cannot hide his thoughts from me."

"But I never thought that—" the psychologist stopped. Suddenly she looked up. "A girl visited him here. She was pretty—blonde and slim. Who was she?"

Herbie answered immediately. "I know the person that you are talking about. She is the cousin of Milton Ashe. He is not in love with her."

Susan Calvin stood up. "I had a dream that he didn't love her," she said happily. She ran to Herbie and held his metal

"You know nothing about human emotions!
You—you are a machine!"

hand in her own hand. "Thank you, Herbie," she whispered. "Don't tell anyone about this. It's our secret. Thank you." And she left the testing room quickly.

———

Milton Ashe slowly stretched his arms and legs. He looked angrily at Peter Bogert.

"I've tested every part of Robot RB-34," he said. "I've worked for a week, and I've had little sleep. You knew what was wrong. That's what you told me. But I haven't found any problems."

"I *do* know what the problem is," said Bogert. "I'm working on it."

"Are you almost finished?" Ashe asked, unpleasantly.

"Unfortunately, Lanning doesn't agree with the theory that I'm using," Bogert replied. "His ideas are out-of-date. He still believes in matrix mechanics. We should use a modern theory to solve this problem."

"Why don't you ask Herbie to help you?" Ashe asked.

"Herbie?" Bogert said, surprised.

"Yes," replied Ashe. "Didn't Calvin tell you? The robot is a mathematical genius[70]."

Bogert looked at Ashe quickly. "Dr Calvin hasn't said this to anyone in *my* department."

"Well, we've talked together about Herbie many times," said Ashe. "I've spent a lot of time with Calvin this week." Ashe frowned. "Bogert...do you think that she's been behaving strangely?"

Bogert smiled. "She's started to wear make-up. Is that what you mean?"

"Yes," Ashe said. "And she looks terrible with that paint on her face. But it's not only her make-up that is strange. Calvin's also talking differently. She talks as if she were happy about something."

"Maybe she's in love," said Bogert, laughing.

"You're crazy," Ashe replied. "Go and speak to Herbie."

"I will," said Bogert. "This robot can't be better at my job than me!"

———

Herbie listened carefully as Bogert spoke.

"I was told that you're a mathematical genius," said Bogert. "My theory has some procedures that Dr Lanning won't accept."

The robot didn't answer.

"Well?" said Bogert.

Herbie studied Bogert's work. "I see no mistakes in your calculations[71]," he said.

"Can you develop my theory any further?" Bogert asked the robot.

"You are better at math than me," the robot answered, and Bogert smiled.

When the mathematician spoke again, he spoke slowly. "Herbie, there's something…maybe you can—" He stopped.

Herbie nodded and Bogert continued. "Lanning is nearly seventy," Bogert said. "He's been the director at this company for nearly thirty years. Is he…er…is he planning to stop work?"

"He has already resigned[72]," the robot said quietly. "But he will not leave the company until he solves the problem of…me."

Bogert sighed. "And who will be the next director?"

"You are the next director," said Herbie.

Bogert smiled. "This is good to know," he said. "I've waited for this news. Thanks, Herbie."

———

Bogert worked until five a.m. After four hours of sleep, he returned to his desk. He wrote many pages of calculations. At midday, he was staring unhappily at the final page, when he heard a knock at the door. Lanning entered the room.

The director looked at the papers that covered Bogert's desk. He frowned. "Has Calvin told you about the robot?" he asked. "Herbie is a mathematical genius. He's amazing."

"I've tested Herbie and he has trouble with some easy calculations," Bogert said.

"Calvin didn't think this, and neither do I," Lanning replied angrily. "I've been with Herbie all morning," he went on. "The robot can do very complex calculations. Look," he gave Bogert a piece of paper. "He's worked on your theory. He agrees with me."

Bogert studied the papers. "Well," he said coldly. "Let *Herbie* solve the whole problem for you."

"But he can't," Lanning replied. "Herbie can't solve the whole problem. We need more experts to help us. I'm going to inform the National Board."

Bogert jumped up. "No, don't!" he said.

"Don't tell me what to do!" said Lanning. "If you don't follow my orders, I'll suspend[73] you."

"No, you won't suspend me, Lanning," Bogert replied. "I know about your resignation."

"What?!" said Lanning. His face showed shock and surprise.

Bogert laughed unpleasantly. "And *I'm* going to be the new director. I'm going to give the orders now."

"You're suspended!" Lanning shouted.

Bogert smiled. "I don't care," he said. "I know that you've resigned. Herbie told me."

Suddenly Lanning looked old and tired. "That's not true," he said, slowly and softly. "I want to speak to Herbie. You're playing a game, Bogert. Come with me."

————

At midday, Ashe was talking to Susan Calvin. He was showing her a picture of a house. "What do you think?" he asked. "It's beautiful, and I have the money to buy it."

Calvin looked at him. "It is beautiful," she agreed. "I've often thought that I'd like to—" She stopped.

Ashe moved his chair closer toward her. "The truth is this," he said. "The house isn't just for me. I'm getting married!" Suddenly he looked more closely at her. "Susan, what's the matter? Are you feeling sick?"

"No...it's nothing!" said Dr Calvin. She could only just speak. "Y–you're getting married?"

"Yes!" said Ashe. "Do you remember the girl who was here last summer? She's going to be my wife. But you *are* sick. You—"

"I have a headache!" Susan Calvin replied. "Congratulations, Ashe! You have my best wishes!" And she ran from the room.

"This is like a bad dream," she thought. "This can't be happening! Herbie said...Oh! Herbie knew! He can read minds!" She had reached the door of the testing room. She leaned against the door and stared at Herbie.

"Yes, you are dreaming," he was saying. His voice was soft and gentle. "You will wake soon. Ashe does love you."

Susan Calvin nodded. "Yes!" she whispered. "It's true, isn't it?" Then she stopped. This was *not* a dream!

"What are you trying to do?" she cried.

"I want to help," Herbie said. There was fear in his voice.

The psychologist stared at the robot. "You wanted to help, but you told me a lie." She stopped. "Wait! I had only..."

"I had to!" the robot said.

"And I believed you!" Calvin cried.

There were loud voices outside the door. Calvin turned away. When Bogert and Lanning entered, she was standing at the window.

The two men went to Herbie. Lanning looked angry, but Bogert was smiling.

"Herbie, listen to me!" said the director. "Have you talked to Dr Bogert about me?"

The robot looked at the director. "No, sir," the robot answered slowly.

The smile on Bogert's face disappeared. "Repeat what you told me yesterday!" he said.

"I said that…" Herbie became silent.

"Answer me!" shouted Bogert.

"I'll ask him," said Lanning. He turned to the robot. "Okay, Herbie, listen carefully. Have I resigned?"

Herbie looked at Lanning, and did not reply. Lanning repeated the question. The robot tried to nod his head, but he could not.

"What's the matter?" Bogert shouted at Herbie. "Can't you speak?"

"I can speak," Herbie answered.

"Then, answer the question," Bogert said angrily. "Did you tell me that Lanning had resigned?"

At the other end of the room, Susan Calvin suddenly laughed. The two mathematicians turned toward her.

"What's so funny?" Bogert asked.

"Nothing's funny." Her voice was sharp. "The three greatest robotics experts all fell into the same trap[74]. But it isn't funny."

"Please explain, Dr Calvin," said Lanning.

"You know the First Law of Robotics, don't you?" she said.

The two men nodded. "Of course," answered Bogert. "A robot may not harm a human. And it must not allow a human to be harmed."

"But what *kind* of harm?" Calvin asked.

"Any kind," Lanning replied.

"Exactly! Any kind of harm!" she said. "A person's body can be hurt, of course. But someone's feelings can be hurt, too. If you hear someone saying unkind words about you, or if you hear bad news, your feelings are hurt. Maybe you expect something to happen, and it doesn't. Then your feelings are hurt. A person can been *harmed* in many ways."

Lanning frowned. "But what would a robot know about—" And then he stopped.

"You understand, don't you?" Calvin said. "This robot reads minds. It knows what people think and want. You ask him a question, and he gives you an answer. But it is the answer that you *want* to hear. Any other answer would hurt you. He knows that."

"And that's why he wouldn't answer before!" said Lanning. "He couldn't answer truthfully, without hurting one of us."

"That…that machine knows everything," said Calvin. "He even knows *why* he can read minds. He knows exactly what went wrong when he was built. His brain changed when he was impressioned."

"Herbie doesn't know what went wrong, Dr Calvin," said Lanning. "I asked him, but he couldn't give me an answer."

"But Herbie *knew* this," said Calvin. "You didn't *want* Herbie to give you the answer. Your feelings would have been hurt if you knew that a machine was better than you."

Calvin turned toward Herbie. "Come here!" she ordered. Herbie walked toward her slowly. "You know what went wrong," she said.

"Yes," Herbie said quietly.

"All right, then, Herbie. Tell us!"

"I cannot tell you what went wrong, Dr Calvin," said the robot. "You know that. Dr Bogert and Dr Lanning do not want me to tell you."

"Tell us," said Lanning.

"No!" Herbie cried. "I know your thoughts. You *do not* want me to tell you. I am a machine. You do not want a machine to be better than you. The answer will hurt you."

"Herbie," said Calvin, "you also know that they want a truthful answer."

"They want to find out for themselves!" Herbie said.

"But they want the answer to the problem," said Calvin.

"You know the answer, and you won't give it to them. That hurts them. You understand this, don't you?"

"Yes!" Herbie cried.

"And if you tell them, that will hurt them, too!" Calvin said and she walked forward.

"Yes! Yes!" Herbie stepped back, as the psychologist came toward him.

"You can't tell them," Calvin said slowly, "because that would hurt them. And you mustn't hurt them. But if you *don't* tell them, you'll hurt them. So you *must* tell them."

Now, Herbie's back was against the wall. Suddenly, he fell down onto his knees. "Stop!" he cried. And he lifted his hands to his head.

But Calvin did not stop talking. "You must tell them," she said in a cold, hard voice. "If you tell them, you'll hurt them. But if you don't tell them, you'll hurt them."

Herbie screamed once, and fell forward. His face was touching the floor.

"He's dead!" said Bogert. His eyes were wide and his face was white.

"No," said Susan Calvin. She laughed. "He's not dead. He's just crazy. I gave him a problem which has no answer."

"You did that deliberately!" Lanning cried. "You wanted to make him crazy!"

"He had to be punished," she said.

The director turned to Bogert. "Come, Peter," he said. And the two men left the testing room.

Susan Calvin did not speak or move for several minutes. Finally, she looked at Herbie and spoke one word.

"LIAR!" she said.

———

I knew that Dr Calvin would say nothing more about this case. She sat in front of me and remembered the past. Her face was white and cold.

"Stop!" he cried. And he lifted his hands to his head.

"Thank you, Dr Calvin!" I said.

I left her, and went to write the notes for my article. Two days passed before I saw her again.

6

Little Lost Robot

W hen I saw Susan Calvin again, it was at the door of her office. Office workers were removing her things.

"Have you finished your article?" she asked.

"Almost," I said. "Would you like to read it? Do you want to see if I've made any mistakes?"

"Very well," she replied.

Dr Calvin seemed happier today. I decided to ask her more about the history of robotics on other worlds.

"What about robots and space travel?" I asked. "Space stations are a little out-of-date now. Robots developed the hyperatomic drive twenty years ago, so that we could travel easily between worlds."

"Space travel?" said Dr Calvin. She thought for a few seconds. "My first experience of traveling in space was in 2029. That was when a robot was lost…"

Susan Calvin had never left Earth before, but now, she was sitting in the Hyper Base space station. The Hyper Base was part of the 27th Astroidal Group of space stations. Dr Calvin had been brought here by a special government spaceship. The mathematical director of U.S. Robots, Dr Peter Bogert, had traveled with her. The robot-psychologist had received a report about a problem with the robots on the Hyper Base. But she was not sure that there really was an emergency. And her feelings about this showed on her face.

The robot-psychologist was sitting with Dr Bogert and General Kallner, the head of the Hyper Base project. Bogert looked unhappy and uncomfortable. Kallner looked extremely worried.

"We've lost a robot," Kallner said. "We've tried everything that we can think of. But we can't find it. We've failed. We need help from experts."

"Why is this one robot so important?" asked Calvin. "And *why* haven't you found it?"

"As soon as the robot disappeared, we started our emergency procedures," Kallner replied. "All work on the hyperatomic drive has stopped. Nobody can enter the Hyper Base without permission. And nobody can leave without permission." The general was silent for a few seconds. Then he went on.

"A few weeks ago, a cargo ship[75] landed. It was delivering two robots for our laboratories," he said. "The ship also contained sixty-two robots of the...same type. We're completely sure of that number. These sixty-two robots were being sent on to another planet."

"Why is this important?" Calvin asked. "And why were emergency procedures started?"

"One of the laboratory robots disappeared," Kallner replied. "When we counted the robots on the cargo ship again, there were sixty-three."

"So, the sixty-third robot is the lost robot?" Calvin said, impatiently.

"Yes, but we don't know *which* robot it is," Kallner explained.

There was silence. Then the robot-psychologist turned to Bogert. "Peter, what's wrong here?" Calvin asked. "What type of robots are they using?"

"Hyper Base is using some modified[76] robots," Bogert said. "Their brains aren't impressioned with the complete First Law of Robotics."

58

"They haven't been completely impressioned with the First Law!" Calvin repeated. She was shocked. She sat back in her chair. "How many modified robots were made?"

"A few," Bogert replied. He looked down at the desk. "They were part of a government order. Only a few people knew about it. It was a secret," he said.

"We *needed* modified robots," said General Kallner. "So, a few of the NS-2 models—the Nestors—were prepared with a modified First Law. This had to be a secret. So all NS-2s were made without identification numbers."

"Have you asked each robot who it is?" Calvin asked Kallner.

The general nodded. "Yes," he said. "All sixty-three robots say that they have not worked here. One is lying. Dr Calvin, we cannot let that cargo ship leave. If people find out that modified robots exist, there—"

"Destroy all sixty-three robots," said the robot-psychologist coldly.

Bogert frowned. "Dr Calvin, we can't just destroy them all," he said. "Each robot costs thirty thousand dollars! First, we have to find the lost modified robot."

"Very well," she said, angrily. "I need facts. Why does Hyper Base need these modified robots, General?"

"We had problems with our previous robots," said Kallner. "The men on the base have to work with radioactive material. It's dangerous, but we're very careful. Humans can stay in gamma radiation for about thirty minutes before they are harmed. Robots know that radiation can harm humans. If one of our men had to work where there was radiation, the nearest robot would run to save him. If the radiation was weak, the robot would successfully carry him away. But if the radiation was strong, it destroyed the robot's positronic brain. No robot can exist without a brain. So we had to stop work until the robots were removed."

"We told the robots, 'You're risking your own existence[77].'" Kallner continued. "But it is only the Third Law of Robotics that allows robots to protect their own lives. It is the First Law of Robotics that is the strongest law. This law says: 'A robot must not harm a human. And it must not allow a human to be harmed.' Next, we ordered the robots to stay out of the gamma radiation. But obeying a human's order is only the Second Law. The First Law is stronger than the Second Law. So we decided to modify the First Law. The modified robots were impressioned with only the first part of the First Law: 'A robot must not harm a human.'"

"Peter," Calvin asked. "Is that the *only* difference between the laboratory robots and the ordinary NS-2 models?"

"It's the *only* difference, Susan," Bogert replied. "They all look the same."

She stood up. "I'm going to sleep now," she said. "Tomorrow, I want to speak to the last person who saw the modified robot."

But Susan Calvin did not sleep much that night. Early the next morning, she knocked on Bogert's door.

"I guess that you're angry about all this," he said.

The psychologist stared at him. "Peter, don't you realize what this means?" she said. "All beings hate to be dominated[78]. And they hate to be dominated by an inferior being. Robots are superior to humans. Robots are stronger and more intelligent. Robots only obey humans *because of the First Law!*"

"But the Law was only modified," he said.

"Are the modified Nestors' brains stable[79]?" she asked.

"Their brains are a little less stable," Bogert said. But he quickly continued. "But they are *safe*. The first Nestors came to the base nine months ago. And nothing has gone wrong with any Nestor, until now. Humans aren't in danger."

"I'll see you at the meeting," Calvin said.

———

Gerald Black, a young scientist of physics, sat across from Calvin and Bogert. He was nervous.

"You know the lost robot—Nestor 10—better than anybody else," Calvin said to Black. "How is the Nestors' behavior different from ordinary robots?" she asked.

"There's nothing especially different about the Nestors," Black said. "Of course, they're much more intelligent. And they're more annoying."

"They're more annoying?" she repeated. "Why do the Nestors make you angry? Have they ever refused to obey an order?"

"Oh, no," Black said quickly. "The Nestors obey our orders. But if they think that you're wrong, they'll tell you. The Nestors only know what we've taught them. But they think that they know *everything*."

"Think about the day that the robot disappeared," said Bogert. "Did anything unusual happen?"

There was a silence. "I had a little problem with Nestor 10," Black said, at last. "He wanted me to repeat a test. He was always saying this. It was very annoying, and I was tired of it. I told him to go away, and he left."

"You told him to go away?" asked Dr Calvin. "What did you say? Try to remember the exact words."

"I said, 'Get lost[80]'," Black replied.

Bogert laughed. "And he did get lost," he said.

"Thank you, Mr Black," said Calvin. "You may go now."

———

Five hours later, Susan Calvin had interviewed the sixty-three robots. All the robots looked the same. Bogert was waiting for her when she finished.

"We'll only find the lost robot when we know how it is different," she said. "We can't let the robot escape. I'll destroy them all, if I have to. Have you spoken to the other modified Nestors?"

"Yes, I have," Bogert said, "and there's nothing wrong with them. They all try to show their superior intelligence. But they're harmless."

"*Are* they harmless?" Calvin said angrily. "*One* of them is lying. That's frightening—and dangerous."

"Listen!" said Bogert. "Black ordered Nestor 10 to get lost, so he disappeared. His hiding place was with the other Nestors. That was very clever."

"The modified Nestors feel superior to other robots," said the robot-psychologist. "The lost robot will want to show its superiority. It thinks that superiority is very important. Soon, the lost robot may believe that superiority is *more* important than never harming a human."

"But it couldn't harm a human, could it?" said Bogert.

The psychologist thought for a moment. "Here's an example. If a modified robot allowed a heavy weight[81] to fall toward a human, he wouldn't be breaking the First Law. This is because he could easily catch the weight before it hit the human. And he would know this. However, when the weight leaves the robot's fingers, it falls because of gravity[82]. At that moment, the robot would no longer be responsible. The robot would not have to do anything. The modified First Law allows the robot to behave in this way. We'll have to test all the robots. We must see how they react[83]. We need to test their reactions to the First Law."

In the center of the Radiation Room, a man sat in a chair. He was not moving, or speaking. Sixty-three Nestor robots were sitting in cubicles[84] that were built in a circle around the man. One side of each cubicle was open. Each robot could see the man in the chair, but it could not see the other robots.

The testing began. A weight dropped from the ceiling. Sixty-three robots ran forward to save the man. Before the weight hit the man, a beam of energy pushed the weight away. At that moment, the robots stopped. The test was repeated ten times. Ten times, the robots ran forward. All of them stopped when they knew that the man was safe.

Kallner and Bogert were in an observation room. They were watching the tests through a window.

"What's happening here?" Kallner asked.

"Sixty-two of these robots will try to save the man," Bogert explained. "They have to do this, because they must obey the First Law. The sixty-third robot—Nestor 10—didn't *have* to try and save the man. He has been modified—the First Law in his brain is not complete. However, he made a choice. The modified robot did what *he* wanted to do. He *chose* to save the man."

"Why?" the general asked.

"I don't know," Bogert said. "I hoped that Nestor 10 would be surprised the first time. I hoped that his reaction would be slow. But it wasn't. And now he's behaving like all the other robots."

"Then we still don't know the truth," the general said unhappily.

Susan Calvin entered the room. "We'll have to try a different test," she said. "And we need to do it quickly. I don't like what's happening. We haven't caught Nestor 10, and he must be feeling very superior. At first, he hid because he was obeying an order. Now, he's hiding because he wants to show that he's superior to humans."

"What is your advice, Dr Calvin?" the general asked.

"We'll repeat the test," she replied. "But we'll put electric beams between the robots and the man. We'll tell the robots that the electrical beams will kill them. We can switch the electricity off. But the robots won't know that."

"Will this test be successful?" asked the general.

"It should be," Calvin said. "The normal robots will try to save the man, although they know that they will die. They have to obey the First Law. Nestor 10 doesn't have the complete First Law, so he doesn't have to save the man. Of course, he has to obey the Second Law. We could *order* him to touch the cables, and die. But he *won't* be ordered to do that. So, he doesn't have to follow the First, or the Second Laws. He'll follow the Third Law, and protect his own existence. He won't do anything."

———

In the Radiation Room, a man sat in the chair, motionless and silent. A weight dropped, but a beam pushed it away from the man at the last moment. In the cubicles, sixty-three robots watched. Not one moved.

In the observation room, Dr Calvin saw this and was horrified.

———

Susan Calvin was interviewing all the robots again. The next robot entered the testing room.

"Sit down. I want to ask you some questions," Calvin said.

The robot sat down.

"There was a man who was almost harmed in the Radiation Room. You did nothing, did you?" she asked.

"That is correct," the robot replied.

"Why didn't you try to save him?" she asked.

"Please don't think that I could *harm* a human," the robot said. "That would be horrible. I knew that the room was dangerous for me. I would have to cross the electric beams to save the man, and I knew that I would die. But...but then I thought again. If I died, I would not be able to save him. I had been given no orders to do this. I would be destroying myself for nothing. That would not be logical behavior."

The robot-psychologist had heard the same story from all the other robots.

"Did you think of this yourself?" she asked.

The robot paused. "No."

"Who thought of it, then?" she asked.

"One of us had the idea last night," the robot replied.

"Which one?" Calvin asked. She waited for several seconds for the reply.

"I don't know," said the robot, at last. "Just one of us."

———

"We have to separate the robots," Calvin said. "They cannot see each other, or talk to each other."

"Dr Calvin," the general replied, "that's impossible. I—"

"Then all the robots must be destroyed," Calvin said, angrily.

"Those robots are *not* going to be destroyed," Bogert said angrily. "*I'm* responsible for them, not you."

"And this problem must be solved," the general said.

Calvin turned to Bogert. "We have one very unstable Nestor, and more that could soon become unstable," she said in a cold, hard voice. "We must destroy them all."

Gerald Black knocked on the door and walked into the room. "I've just returned from the cargo ship," he said. "I found some marks on the door locks, in Area C of the ship."

"Area C?" Calvin said quickly. "The Nestors are in there, aren't they? Who made the marks?"

"The marks were on the *inside* of the door of Area C," Black explained. "Two of my men, Robbins and McAdams, are guarding the door now."

"What does this mean?" Kallner asked.

"This means that Nestor 10 is planning to leave the base," Calvin replied. "He's trying to break the locks. He could easily steal a spaceship and leave with it. Then we'd have a crazy robot on a spaceship. What would he do next? I have no idea, General. The Nestor 10 is the same as the normal robots, except—" she stopped suddenly.

65

"What is it?" Kallner looked at her.

"I've got an idea," Calvin said. She turned toward Black. "You taught Nestor 10 all that he knows. Is that true?"

"Yes. I taught him about physics," Black replied. "He worked with me in the laboratory. None of the other Nestors know about physics."

"Why aren't the modified Nestors impressioned with physics before they come here?"

"We thought that people would be suspicious[85] if some Nestors already knew physics," the general explained.

"Please leave, all of you," said Calvin. "I need to prepare a new test."

————

Before the test began, Bogert told the robots what was going to happen. He interviewed each robot alone. And every interview was the same.

"We're going to do another test," Bogert said. "A man will be in danger. However, between the man and yourself, there will be gamma radiation. Do you know what gamma radiation is?"

"It is a type of electromagnetic radiation that produces high energy," said every robot.

"Have you ever worked with gamma radiation?" asked Bogert.

"No, sir." Every robot's reply was quick and strong.

"Well, gamma radiation will kill you instantly," Bogert said.

"But sir," said the robots, "if there is gamma radiation between myself and the man, how can I save him? When I try to save him, I would no longer exist. And the man would die. That is illogical and unnecessary."

"Yes…" Bogert said slowly. "If you detect[86] gamma radiation between yourself and the man, do not move. This is my advice."

"Thank you, sir," said the robots.

"However," said Bogert, "if you *don't* detect dangerous radiation, and the weight falls, you must try to save the man."

"Of course, sir," each robot said.

"Leave now. You'll be taken to a room. You'll wait there, alone, until we are ready."

———

The large Radiation Room was ready once more. The robots waited patiently.

"Have any of the robots spoken to each other?" Calvin asked.

"No," Black said. "They haven't seen or spoken to each other."

"Good," said Calvin. "They'll be in front of me," she explained to Bogert and the general. "If any robot behaves strangely, I'll see immediately."

"*You're* going to sit in the chair?" Bogert said, surprised.

"Yes," she said. "Peter, you'll sit in the observation room. I want you to watch the robots that are behind me. Let's try the test again. I hope that this will be the last time."

———

Susan Calvin went into the Radiation Room, sat in the chair, and the test began.

The heavy weight fell. At the last moment, one robot jumped from his seat, and ran toward Dr Calvin.

But before the robot reached Dr Calvin, the energy beam pushed the weight away from her.

Dr Calvin stood up and pointed at the robot. "Nestor 10, come here!" she cried. "COME HERE!"

Slowly, the robot took another step. The psychologist watched the robot.

"Get the other robots out of here!" Calvin called to the men in the observation room. "Get them out quickly, and *keep* them out."

67

One robot jumped from his seat and ran toward Dr Calvin.

Nestor 10 stepped forward again. And then he spoke. "I was told to get lost!" He took another step. "I must obey. They have not found me yet. Now, Black will think that I am a failure. But I am not. I am powerful and clever." He took another step. "I have superior intelligence. And now I have been found by a weak human!"

Suddenly he put his metal arm on Susan Calvin's neck, and pushed her down. She heard the robot speak, but she could not reply. She could not breathe.

"Nobody must find me," said Nestor 10.

Suddenly, there was a strange sound, and Dr Calvin was on the ground. Nestor 10 was lying beside her.

"Are you hurt, Dr Calvin?" Black cried.

The psychologist coughed and began to breathe again. "No," she said, at last. Black helped her to stand.

"What happened?" she asked.

"We realized that he was attacking[87] you," Black explained. "So I sent gamma radiation into the room, for five seconds. There was no time to do anything else. The radiation killed Nestor 10, but it didn't harm you. A small amount of gamma radiation is harmless for humans."

"I don't think that Nestor 10 really attacked me," Calvin said slowly. "He was *trying* to attack me, but the first part of the First Law stopped him."

———

Two weeks after they had come to Hyper Base, Calvin and Bogert had their final meeting with General Kallner.

The work on Hyper Base had started again. And the cargo ship had left with the other sixty-two Nestors. A government ship was waiting to take the two robot experts back to Earth.

"Will the other modified Nestors be destroyed?" Calvin asked.

"Yes," Kallner agreed. "But please tell me. Why was the last test successful?"

She smiled. "Nestor 10 thought that he was superior to humans," she said. "He thought that he and the other robots knew more than humans. And we knew that Nestor 10 thought this way. So we told all the robots that gamma radiation would kill them. In the previous test, the robots had made a decision. They wouldn't save the human. This is because they knew that they might die if they tried. So the robots didn't try to save me."

"I understand that, Dr Calvin," said General Kallner. "But why did Nestor 10 move?" he asked.

"Because we used heat radiation in the test. We didn't use gamma radiation," said the robot-psychologist. "Normal Nestors can't tell the difference between types of radiation. They haven't been taught physics. Only Nestor 10 knew the difference, because he was taught the science by Gerald Black. When Nestor 10 realized that there was heat radiation in the room, he knew that it was harmless. He knew that we were lying, so he moved. But he forgot that the other robots might know less than humans. He was caught because he felt so superior. Goodbye, General."

7

Evidence

*S*usan Calvin and I started talking about the changes on Earth in the last fifty years.

"I remember when the hyperatomic drive was invented," Dr Calvin said. "That was before we could travel far into space, to other worlds.

"By the early 2030s, there were too many people and too many governments on Earth. And there were too many nations," she went *on.* "*At last, the nations joined together into larger groups. They became regions. When I was born, the United States of America was a nation. Now it is part of the Northern Region. Robots were responsible for the change.*"

"*You mean the Machines,*" I said.

"*Yes,*" *she replied. Suddenly her voice was sad.* "*But I wasn't thinking of the Machines, I was thinking of a man who died last year. In fact, he planned his death. He knew that we didn't need him any longer. His name was Stephen Byerley.*"

"*Byerley became a member of the government in 2032,*" *she went on.* "*You were only a boy then. You won't remember this. He was elected[88] as mayor in 2032. And his election was really strange…*"

———

Francis Quinn was a politician. He had come to Alfred Lanning's office to talk to him.

"Dr Lanning, do you know Stephen Byerley?" Quinn asked.

"No," Lanning replied. "But I know about him."

"Will you vote for him in the next election?" Quinn said.

"I don't know," said Lanning. "I didn't realize that he was a candidate in the election."

"He may be our next mayor," Quinn replied. "Of course, he's only a lawyer now. But—"

"Yes," said Lanning impatiently, "but what do you want from me?"

"I don't want Byerley to become mayor," Quinn answered. "And I don't think that U.S. Robots wants him to become mayor, either."

"I don't understand," Lanning said.

"There's nothing unusual about Byerley's past," said Quinn. "His early life was normal. He grew up in a small town, and attended college. Byerley's wife died when she was only twenty-two. Soon after this, Byerley had a bad car accident.

71

He became a lawyer and then moved to the city. But there *is* one strange thing about his life—he never eats."

Lanning stared at Quinn. He was very surprised.

"Byerley never eats," Quinn said again. "Never! Do you understand what that means?"

"Are you sure?" Lanning asked.

"Yes," said Quinn. "Nobody has *ever* seen him eat or drink anything. And he doesn't sleep."

Lanning leaned back in his chair. "What you're suggesting is impossible," he said.

"Stephen Byerley is a robot, Dr Lanning," Quinn said.

"That's impossible, Mr Quinn," said Lanning again.

There was a silence, then Quinn spoke. "Your company has to test him," he said.

"No, Mr Quinn," Lanning replied, "why should U.S. Robots test him?"

"You have no choice," Quinn said. "If anyone finds out that he is a robot before you complete the tests, your company will be in trouble. U.S. Robots is the only company in the Solar System that makes positronic robots. They're the most advanced robots that were ever built. If Byerley is a robot, then he must be a positronic robot. And U.S. Robots is responsible for him."

"But we have never made a robot that looks exactly like a human—a humanoid robot," Lanning said.

"Can it be done?" Quinn asked. "Could someone build a humanoid robot?"

"Yes, it can be done," Lanning replied, "but the inventor would need a positronic brain. When our robots break or fail, we use their positronic brains again, or they're destroyed. That is the law. The government makes U.S. Robots do this."

"But maybe someone stole a positronic brain and made a humanoid robot," Quinn said.

"Impossible!" Lanning cried.

"Soon, the government and the people will make you test Byerley. Why not do it now?" Quinn said calmly.

Lanning sighed. "Very well," he said.

———

Stephen Byerley was forty years old. He looked healthy and happy. Lanning watched Byerley, as he laughed at Lanning's question.

Lanning frowned and looked at Dr Calvin, who was sitting next to him.

"Dr Lanning," said Byerley, laughing again, "you think that I might be a…what?!"

"Someone has told us that you're a robot," replied Lanning. "Only U.S. Robots makes intelligent robots, so we have to find out the truth. The idea that you, a politician, might be a robot could harm the company. It doesn't have to be true. People would protest and the company would be harmed."

"I understand," Byerley replied. "The idea is crazy, but you are in a difficult position. How can I help you?"

"It's simple," Lanning said. "Eat a meal, in a restaurant, where people can see you."

He sat back in his seat. Susan Calvin watched Byerley, but said nothing.

Byerley looked at the woman. "I do not think that I can do that," he said. "I do not sleep much, that is true. And I have never enjoyed eating with other people. This is unusual, but it harms nobody. Did Francis Quinn tell you that I was a robot? His suggestion is nonsense. He does not want me to be elected as mayor. This is his reason for saying this."

"Maybe the suggestion is nonsense," said Lanning. "But if you eat a meal in a restaurant, the questions will stop."

Byerley turned to Susan Calvin. "You are a psychologist and you work for U.S. Robots, don't you?"

"I'm a *robot*-psychologist," she said.

"Are robots very different from men?" Byerley asked.

"Completely different," she said, coldly.

Byerley smiled. "Dr Calvin, I guess that you have brought some food with you."

"You surprise me, Mr Byerley," Calvin said. She opened her bag and took out an apple. She gave it to him, without speaking.

Lanning watched carefully as Byerley calmly ate the apple.

"Eating the apple doesn't prove that you're a robot, or a human," said Susan Calvin.

"Does it not?" said Byerley, smiling.

"Of course not," said Calvin. She turned to the director of U.S. Robots. "Dr Lanning, if Mr Byerley is a humanoid robot, he's a very, very good model. Look at the shape of his face, his skin, and his eyes. If he *is* a robot, I wish that U.S. Robots *had* made him. He's perfect. And a perfect humanoid robot would be able to eat."

"I'm not an idiot," Lanning said angrily. "I don't care if Mr Byerley is human or not. I want to protect the company. That's the only thing that interests me. He has to eat a whole meal in a restaurant. Then people will see the truth."

"Dr Lanning," Byerley said, "Both Quinn and I want to win the election. Quinn wants to stop me. If he wants to call me a robot, he can. But he will never *prove* that I am a robot."

———

Byerley arrived home and went into the sitting room. The man in a wheelchair[89] looked up at him, and smiled.

Byerley smiled and touched the man's shoulder.

"You're late, Steve," the man said. His voice was weak and he had many scars on his face.

"I am sorry, John," said Byerley. "I have a problem and I may need your help."

"Let's go into the yard," Byerley went on. "It is a beautiful evening."

He lifted John from the wheelchair. Then he carried him into the yard, and put him down carefully on the cool grass.

"Tell me about your problem," John said.

"Quinn has started his election campaign. He is going to tell everyone that I am a robot."

"How do you know this?" replied John.

"Two scientists from U.S. Robots came to see me today," Byerley said. "They told me."

"What are you going to do, Steve?"

"I have a plan," Byerley answered. "Listen, and tell me if it will work."

———

Francis Quinn stared at Alfred Lanning. "Byerley is not being truthful," said the politician.

"If you're wrong, what will you do?" Lanning asked. "We've seen him eat. He isn't a robot—that story is nonsense."

"Do *you* think that Byerley is human?" Quinn asked Calvin. "Lanning said that you were the expert."

Susan Calvin looked at Quinn with her cold, bright eyes.

"There are only two ways to prove that Byerley is a robot," she said. "You have to look inside his body, or study his mind. You can cut him open, or use an X-ray[90] to look inside his body. You can study his mind to find out how it is different from a human mind. If Byerley *is* a positronic robot, then he must obey the three Laws of Robotics. Do you know the Laws, Mr Quinn?"

"I've heard about them," Quinn replied.

"If Byerley disobeys one of the three laws, then he's not a robot," said the psychologist. "However, if he obeys all the laws, he *could* be a robot. Or he could simply be a very good man. It's impossible to tell the difference between a superior robot, and the very best humans."

"So you can never prove that Byerley is a robot," said

Quinn. "Is that what you are telling me, Dr Calvin?"

"Maybe I can prove that he's *not* a robot."

"I don't want you to do that," Quinn said. "Dr Lanning, is it possible to create a humanoid robot?"

"Yes," Lanning replied.

"Then we will see what's inside Mr Byerley," Quinn said, and he left.

Lanning turned to Susan Calvin. "Why did you—"

"I won't tell lies for you," Calvin said sharply.

"But what will we do if Byerley is opened up, and we discover that he's a robot?" asked Lanning.

"That won't happen," said Calvin. "Byerley is as clever as Quinn. In fact, he's more intelligent than Quinn."

———

A week before the election campaign began, there was a news report about Stephen Byerley. It said that Byerley might be a robot. At first people laughed. But then, slowly, they began to ask questions.

Was this possible? If the story were true, it would be terrible!

People began to protest. Guards stood outside the offices of U.S. Robots. The police protected Stephen Byerley's home.

A detective, named Harroway, arrived at Byerley's house with two police officers. He was holding a document in his hand. "Mr Byerley, I've come to search your house," he said. He gave Byerley the paper. "Here's a search warrant. We have permission to search the house for...mechanical men or robots."

Byerley looked at the warrant. "Very well," he said. "Search the house."

The officers began to search the house. Harroway turned to Byerley. "Mr Byerley, we have to search *you*," he said.

"Do you mean that you have to X-ray me?" Byerley asked. "Let me read the warrant again." He looked at the document.

"It says that you can search my house. It does not say that you can X-ray me," he said.

"You know the law well," Harroway replied, smiling. Then he called the officers, and left. When he reached his car, Harroway took a tiny machine from his pocket. He looked at the screen on the front of the machine. It was the first time that Harroway had taken an X-ray photo.

———

Quinn called Byerley on the videophone. "I'm going to tell everyone that you're wearing special clothes that block X-rays," he said. "They'll realize that they can't take X-ray photos of you."

"Why will this trouble me?" Byerley replied calmly.

"Because everyone will say that you're afraid of an X-ray," replied Quinn. "People will say that you're hiding a secret."

"And the people will also know that you broke the law," Byerley said. "They will realize that you did something without permission. When I am elected, people will see that I am honest and truthful. They will see that I do not break laws."

"When your house was searched, someone was missing," Quinn said, unpleasantly.

"Yes," Byerley said. "My old teacher. He lives with me, but he's been away. He has been unwell. He is resting in the country."

"Is this man a scientist?" Quinn asked.

"He used to be a lawyer," Byerley said. "But he had an accident. Now he studies biophysics. The government has given him permission to do this work."

"And what does this…teacher…know about robots?" Quinn asked. "Can he build a robot? Is he able to get a positronic brain?"

"Ask your friends at U.S. Robots," Byerley replied. "They would know."

"I think that your teacher is the *real* Stephen Byerley," Quinn said. "And I think that *you* are the robot that he created."

"Really? Then prove it," Byerley said.

"We can search your teacher's house in the country," said Quinn. "I'm sure that we'll find the truth there."

"My teacher is a sick man," Byerley said. "It will be difficult to get a search warrant from the police."

After a few moments, Quinn spoke again. "Why don't you stop your campaign for election, Byerley? You can't win."

"I think that I can," Byerley said.

"Break one of the Three Laws of Robotics," Quinn said. "This will prove that you aren't a robot. But you won't be able to break any of the Three Laws. And so, people will believe that you *are* a robot."

———

One week before the election, Byerley's teacher returned from the country. But he did not return to Byerley's home. A car took him to a house in a different part of the city.

"Stay here, until the election campaign is finished," Byerley told him.

"Do you think that there's any danger?" John asked.

"No. I do not really expect danger," Byerley said. "But if you are here, I will not worry about you. Did anyone give you trouble in the country?"

"Nobody," John said.

"And did everything go well for you?" Byerley asked.

"Yes, there won't be any problems," John replied.

"Good," said Byerley. "Take care of yourself, and watch the television tomorrow."

———

Lenton, Byerley's election campaign manager, was worried. His job had been very difficult. Byerley would not listen to Lenton's advice.

"I am going to talk to the people," Byerley said.

"You can't, Steve!" Lenton said, worried. "There are

too many protestors in the city. They won't listen to your arguments. Quinn has made them angry and frightened. It will be too dangerous for you."

"I am not in danger," Byerley said.

"Not in danger?" Lenton repeated. "There will be fifty thousand protesters downtown. They want all robots to be destroyed. They think that *you* are a robot! They won't listen to you. They'll attack you!"

———

The huge crowd of people filled the downtown area. And millions of people were watching on television. The news about the election had been told all around the world. Everyone wanted to know if Quinn was right. *Was* Stephen Byerley a robot?

The people shouted and screamed angrily. Byerley went on speaking, but they would not listen to him.

Suddenly, Byerley saw a thin man at the front of the crowd. He was trying to say something to Byerley.

Byerley leaned forward. "I cannot hear you," he said. "Come up here. If you have a question, I will answer it."

When the crowd saw the thin man standing beside Byerley, they slowly became quieter. At last there was silence.

"Do you have a question?" Byerley asked.

The thin man stared at Byerley. "You say that you're not a robot!" he shouted. "Then prove it! Hit me! You can't hit a human, you…monster!"

Everyone waited and watched.

"I have no reason to hit you," Byerley said.

The thin man laughed loudly. "You *can't* hit me!" he shouted. "You *won't* hit me. You're not human. You're a monster."

Then suddenly and quickly, Stephen Byerley moved. In front of the crowd, and in front of millions of people who were watching on television, he hit the man. He lifted his hand and hit the thin man on his chin. The man fell to the ground.

He lifted his hand and hit the thin man on his chin.

"I am sorry," Byerley said. He gently lifted the man and turned to the guards. "Please take him inside. I want to speak to him later."

Susan Calvin had seen Byerley hit the man. Now she started to drive away. Suddenly, a reporter ran after the robot-psychologist and shouted a question at her.

"Yes, he's human," she replied.

The reporter left immediately. Nobody listened to the rest of Byerley's speech.

———

Dr Calvin and Stephen Byerley met only once more. It was the week before Byerley became mayor. And it was late—past midnight.

"You don't look tired," said Calvin.

Byerley smiled. "Do not tell Quinn," he said, "but I may not sleep for a long time."

"I won't tell him," she replied. "However, Quinn's theory was interesting. Was it true?" she asked.

"Parts of his theory were true," he replied. "Stephen Byerley was a young lawyer. He wanted everyone to live better lives. He was interested in politics, and he argued well. He was also good at biophysics. But Stephen Byerley had a terrible accident, and he was hurt very badly. He had many scars on his face and body. Soon after the accident, he disappeared. Somehow, he got a positronic brain and grew a body around it. He created the most advanced robot of all, and he taught it to be like himself. Then he named the machine, Stephen Byerley, and sent it out into the world. Byerley, himself, stayed in his hiding place and became a teacher. Nobody ever saw—"

"Then Quinn's theory was destroyed when you hit a man," Calvin said quickly. "How did that happen?"

"Quinn does not know this, but he helped me," Byerley replied. "My men told people that I had never hit anyone. 'If Stephen Byerley refuses to hit someone, that will prove that he is a robot,' said my men. This was my plan, and this is what my men told everyone. Next, I decided to make a speech. I guessed that someone would test me with the Laws of Robotics. Someone would tell me to hit him. And that is what happened. Of course, after that I was elected."

The robot-psychologist nodded. "I like robots," she said. "I like robots more than humans. I think that a robot would be an excellent politician. A robot would be truthful, careful and fair. And he wouldn't be able to harm humans. A robot would be an excellent leader."

"But a robot might fail because his brain is not as complex as a human brain," Byerley said.

"People can give him advice," Calvin said. "Even human politicians cannot succeed without advisors." She smiled.

"Why are you smiling, Dr Calvin?" Byerley said.

"Because an important part of Mr Quinn's theory was wrong," she replied.

"What do you mean?" Byerley asked.

"Quinn forgot one important thing," said Calvin.

"I do not understand," Byerley said.

Dr Calvin stood up. "There's one time when a robot can hit a man, without breaking the First Law. Just one time," she said.

"And when is that?" Byerley asked.

Dr Calvin went toward the door. "When the 'man' is another robot," she said quietly, and smiled. "Goodbye, Mr Byerley. Five years from now, there'll be an election for the position of Regional Coordinator. I hope that you're elected."

———

I stared at Susan Calvin. I was horrified. "Is that true?" I asked. "Was Byerley a robot?"

"We can never be completely sure," she replied. "I think that he was. But when he died, Byerley's body was destroyed. Nobody

will ever be able to prove if he was a robot, or a human. Anyway, it wasn't a problem, was it?"

"Well…" I said.

"Stephen Byerley was a very good mayor. And five years later, he did become Regional Coordinator," Calvin said. "And when the Regions of Earth formed the Federation, in 2044, he became the first World Coordinator. And by that time, the Machines were controlling everything."

"But—" I stopped.

"And that is all," said Dr Calvin, as she stood up. "I saw how robots were developed. In the beginning, they couldn't speak and men were their masters. Now robots are extremely clever and powerful. They control the lives of humans. It will be the Machines who decide who lives, and who dies. I'm old and tired. My life will soon end. Young man, you'll see what comes next."

I never saw Susan Calvin again. She died last month, at the age of eighty-two.

Points for Understanding

1

1 Look at the Three Laws of Robotics on page 9. Give the meanings of
   these words. Explain why they are important in the laws.
   (a) *harm* (b) *conflict* (c) *protect*
2 Describe Susan Calvin.
3 Why is the reporter interviewing her?

2

1 What do these people think of Robbie?
   (a) Gloria (b) Grace Weston (c) George Weston. Give reasons.
2 Why does Mr Weston arrange for the family to go on a trip to the
   U.S. Robots factory in New York?
3 What happens there?
4 Robbie is a robot. Do you think that he has feelings? Give reasons.

3

1 What problem do Powell and Donovan have on Solar Station 5?
2 Why does Cutie not believe that Powell and Donovan created him?
   Who *does* he believe created him?
3 What do Powell and Donovan think will happen during the electron
   storm? What happens?

4

1 Describe Dave.
2 What is the problem with Dave?
3 How do Powell and Donovan solve the problem?

5

1 What special power does Herbie have?
2 How does he use this power on these people? (a) Susan Calvin
   (b) Alfred Lanning (c) Peter Bogert (d) Milton Ashe
3 Why does the robot behave in this way?
4 How and why does Susan Calvin destroy Herbie?

6

1 How and why were the Nestors modified?
2 Why was the Nestor 10 lost?
3 The scientists did three tests. Why are these things important?
   (a) cubicles (b) heat radiation (c) gamma radiation
4 Did the tests succeed, or fail? Why?
5 Why did Nestor 10 move on the third test?

7

1 Why does Quinn tell the story about Byerley?
2 Susan Calvin says that there are two ways to prove that Byerley is a
   robot. What are they?
3 What happens when Byerley is speaking to the huge crowd? How
   does this show that he is not a robot?
4 What was Quinn's theory?
5 Why does Susan Calvin still think that Byerley might be a robot?

Glossary

NOTE: this book is written in American English. Distances are measured in *inches, feet, yards* and *miles*. (1 inch = 25.39 millimeters, 1 foot = 30.47 centimeters, 1 yard = 0.91 meters, 1 mile = 1.60 kilometers.) Weights are measured in *ounces, pounds* and *tons*. (1 ounce = 28.34 grams, 1 pound = 453.59 grams, 1 ton = 907.18 kilograms.) 1 billion = 1 thousand millions. (British English = 1 million millions.)

1 **gained** – *to gain something* (page 4)
   to get or achieve something, usually as a result of a lot of effort.
2 **biochemistry** (page 4)
   the study of chemical processes in living things. Later, Asimov began to study *biophysics*, the study of biological processes using the laws of physics.
3 **divorced** – *to divorce* (page 4)
   to take legal action to end your marriage to someone.
4 **out-of-date** (page 5)
   old and no longer useful.
5 **space** (page 5)
   all of the universe outside the Earth's atmosphere. A *space station* is a laboratory in space where people can live for long periods.
6 **explored** – *to explore something* (page 5)
   to travel around an area in order to learn about it, or in order to search for something valuable such as oil.
7 **exist** (page 5)
   to be present in a particular place, time, or situation. The state of being a real or living thing, or of being present in a particular place, time, or situation, is called *existence*.
8 **man-made satellite** (page 5)
   an object that is sent into space to travel around the Earth in order to receive and send information.
9 **launched** – *to launch something* (page 5)
   to send a space vehicle, missile, or other object into space or into the air.
10 **astronaut** (page 5)
   someone who travels in space.
11 **the solar system** (page 5)
   the Sun and the group of planets that move around it.

12 **invented** – *to invent something* (page 5)
   to design or create something that did not exist before.
13 **obey** (page 6)
   to do what a person, law, or rule says that you must do.
14 **energy** (page 7)
   electricity and other forms of power used for making things work.
15 **harm** (page 9)
   to injure, damage, or have a bad effect on someone or something.
   If you *hurt* someone, you cause someone physical pain or injury.
   Something or someone that is *harmless* does not cause any harm.
16 **conflicts** – *to conflict with something* (page 9)
   if different statements or suggestions conflict, they cannot all be
   right or they cannot all happen.
17 **protect** (page 9)
   to keep someone or something safe. The process of keeping
   someone or something safe is called *protection*. A robot has to keep
   itself safe.
18 **development** (page 9)
   the process of creating a new product or method, or the product
   or method that is created. The verb *to develop something* means to
   create a new product or method.
19 **demonstrate** (page 9)
   to show someone how to do something or how something works.
20 **the case of** (page 11)
   a situation that involves a particular person or thing.
21 **taken apart** – *to take something apart* (page 11)
   to separate an object into its pieces.
22 **banged** – *to bang* (page 11)
   to move with a lot of force, making a loud noise.
23 **impatient** (page 13)
   someone who is *impatient* is annoyed because something is not
   happening as quickly as they want or in the way that they want.
   Someone who is *patient* is able to wait for a long time or deal with a
   difficult situation without becoming angry or upset.
24 **sighed** – *to sigh* (page 14)
   to breathe out slowly making a long soft sound, especially because
   you are disappointed, tired, annoyed, or relaxed.
25 **nervous** (page 14)
   feeling excited and worried, or slightly afraid.
26 **expedition** (page 14)
   a long trip to a dangerous or distant place.

27 **get rid of** (page 15)

to throw away, give away, or sell something that you no longer want or need.

28 **stratosphere** (page 17)

the part of the Earth's atmosphere that is 6 miles (10km) to 31 miles (50km) above the surface.

29 **submarine** (page 17)

a ship that can travel both on the surface of the water and under water.

30 **tractor** (page 19)

a vehicle that is used on farms and in factories for pulling machines.

31 **protested** – *to protest* (page 20)

to show publicly that you oppose something.

32 **banned** – *to ban something* (page 20)

to say officially that something is illegal or not allowed.

33 **model** (page 20)

a particular type of vehicle or machine that a company makes.

34 **experimental** (page 21)

using new ideas or methods that you have not tried before.

35 **illogical** (page 22)

not sensible, or not based on clear facts or reasons. The opposite is *logical*. *Logic* is the study of the way that ideas can be connected and used to explain things.

36 **dot** (page 22)

something that looks very small because it is far away.

37 **planets... and... stars** (page 22)

A *star* is a very large hot ball of gas that appears as a small bright light in the sky at night. A *planet* is a very large round object that moves around the sun or around another star.

38 **ran** – *to run something* (page 24)

to control and organize something such as a business, organization, or event.

39 **radiation** (page 24)

a form of energy that is produced during a nuclear reaction, used for making electrical power. The useless substances that are left after using radiation to produce electrical power is *radioactive* – it contains *radiation* – and is called *radioactive waste*. It is harmful to living things. There are different kinds of *radiation*. *Gamma radiation* is a type of radiation that can pass through solid objects. It is harmless to living things but will kill the robots. *Electromagnetic radiation* is created by electricity, and *heat radiation* is created by heat

– the energy that is produced when the temperature of something changes.

40 *advanced* (page 24)
based on the most recent methods or ideas.

41 *absorb* (page 25)
to take in heat, light, liquid, or some other substance.

42 *efficiently* (page 25)
working well and producing good results by using the available time, money, supplies, etc. in the most effective way.

43 *superior* (page 25)
of high quality, or better or bigger than something else. The opposite is *inferior*.

44 *serve* (page 25)
to do a job, or to perform duties for a person or organization.

45 *humming* – *to hum* (page 26)
to make a low continuous sound.

46 *prophet* (page 27)
someone who is believed to have been sent by God to lead people and teach religious beliefs. The robots believe that the Master is their god who has sent Cutie to be their leader.

47 *fix* (page 27)
to repair something.

48 *replacement* (page 30)
someone or something that takes the place of another person or thing, or the process of replacing someone or something.

49 *data* (page 31)
information that is used for making calculations or decisions.

50 *spacesuit* (page 32)
a set of clothes that allows people to move and breathe in space.

51 *air lock* (page 32)
a small room with controlled air pressure that you use to move between two places with different air pressure.

52 *mine* (page 32)
a large hole or tunnel in the ground from which people take coal, gold, etc. The process of getting coal, gold, etc. from under the ground is called *mining*. The robots *mine* for *ore* – rock or earth from which metal can be obtained.

53 *asteroid* (page 32)
a mass of rock that moves around in space.

54 *rabbit* (page 33)
a small animal with long ears, soft fur, and a short tail.

55 **supervision** (page 33)
If you *supervise*, you are in charge of people and check that they are behaving or working correctly. This activity is called *supervision*.

56 **shift** (page 34)
a period of work time in a place where some people work during the day and some work at night.

57 **marching** – to *march* (page 36)
when soldiers march, they walk in a group with each person matching the speed and movements of the others.

58 **tunnel** (page 36)
a passage through a hill or under the ground.

59 **ledge** (page 37)
a narrow surface that sticks out from the side of a cliff or wall.

60 **cave-in** (page 38)
if a roof or wall *caves in*, it falls down or inward. This is called a *cave-in*.

61 **blast** (page 38)
If you *blast* something, you damage or destroy it with a bomb or gun. The robots *blast* the rock to make the tunnel bigger and find the ore.

62 **emergency** (page 39)
an unexpected situation in which immediate action is necessary, often because there is danger.

63 **shoot** (page 41)
to hit someone or something with a bullet from a gun.

64 **mind-reading** (page 44)
A *mind-reading* robot is able to know what someone is thinking. It can *read* – understand what is happening in – people's minds.

65 **procedure** (page 45)
a way of doing something, especially the correct or usual way.

66 **expert** (page 45)
someone who has a particular skill or knows a lot about a particular subject.

67 **affected** – to *affect something or someone* (page 46)
to change or influence something, often in a negative way.

68 **theory** (page 46)
an idea that explains how or why something happens.

69 **complex** (page 46)
containing many details or small parts and therefore difficult to understand or deal with.

70 **genius** (page 49)
someone who is much more intelligent or skillful than other people.

71 **calculation** (page 50)
numbers or symbols that you write when you are calculating
something, or the process of calculating something.

72 **resigned** – *to resign* (page 50)
to state formally that you are leaving your job.

73 **suspend** (page 51)
to order someone to leave their job or school for a short period of
time as a punishment.

74 **fell into the same trap** – *to fall into a trap* (page 53)
a *trap* is a trick that is designed to catch someone or make them
do something that they did not mean to do. If you make a mistake
because someone has tricked you, you *fall into a trap*.

75 **cargo ship** (page 58)
a very large boat that is used for carrying goods long distances.

76 **modified** – *to modify something* (page 58)
to change something slightly in order to improve it or in order to
make it less extreme.

77 **risking your existence** – *to risk your existence* (page 60)
if you *risk your life*, you put yourself in a situation in which you
could be killed. The robots are not alive, but they *exist* and they are
putting themselves in a situation in which they could stop existing.

78 **dominated** – *to dominate someone or something* (page 60)
to control someone or something by having more power or
influence.

79 **stable** (page 60)
having a healthy mental and emotional state. The opposite is
unstable.

80 **get lost** (page 61)
used for telling someone rudely to go away.

81 **weight** (page 62)
a heavy object.

82 **gravity** (page 62)
the force that makes something fall to the ground.

83 **react** – *to react* (page 62)
to behave in a particular way because of things that are happening
around you or things that other people are doing to you. The way
that you feel or behave as a result of something that happens is
called a *reaction*.

91

84 **cubicle** (page 62)

a small enclosed area in a room.

85 **suspicious** (page 66)

if you are *suspicious*, you do not trust someone or you think that something bad might have happened.

86 **detect** – *to detect* (page 66)

to notice or prove that something is present by using scientific methods.

87 **attacking** – *to attack someone or something* (page 69)

to use violence against a person or place.

88 **elected** – *to elect someone* (page 71)

to choose someone to represent you or to hold an official position, by voting for them in an *election*. The people who are competing in an election are called *candidates*, and they try to win by a series of actions called an *election campaign*. The *campaign manager's* job is to organize the campaign. Byerley was elected as *mayor* – the most important elected official in a town or city.

89 **wheelchair** (page 74)

a chair with large wheels that someone who cannot walk uses to move around.

90 **X-ray** (page 75)

X-rays are a type of radiation that is used for looking inside things such as your body. A picture of the inside of someone's body that is taken using X-rays is also called an *X-ray*.

Dictionary extracts adapted from the Macmillan Essential Dictionary © Bloomsbury Publishing PLC 2002 and © A & C Black Publishers Ltd 2005.

Exercises

Vocabulary: words in the story

Choose the best word in the following sentences.

> **Example:** He ~~won~~ / gained / ~~scored~~ a degree in chemistry.

1 Russian scientists lifted / shot / launched Sputnik 1 in 1957.

2 Asimov invented / thought / made some special words for his stories.

3 A robot must not keep / protect / harm a human being.

4 The Third Law must not conflict / agree / obey with the first two laws.

5 Robots must take / protect / put themselves from danger.

6 The development / creation / completion of robots continued and the designs improved.

7 Between 2003 and 2007, most governments on Earth banned / burned / destroyed robots.

8 DV-5 robots were used to mean / mine / main ore from under the ground.

9 The robots did not have to be told / looked / supervised by humans while they worked.

10 In the event of an accident, we have emergency procedures / talks / protection that work automatically.

11 A robot's brain is not as complete / complex / common as a human brain – it is simpler.

12 Bogert was told to leave his job for a time – he was resigned / temporary / suspended.

13 Robots are better than humans – robots are inferior / superior / cooler to humans.

14 The positronic brains of the Nestors are less able / manageable / stable than human brains.

93

15 He was <u>elevated / ejected / elected</u> as mayor.

16 We thought that people might not trust Nestor models – we thought that people might be <u>suspect / suspicious / suggestive</u> of them.

Writing: rewriting sentences

Use words from the box to rewrite these sentences. You may need to change some verb tenses. There are two extra words that you do not need.

~~intelligent~~   faithful   population   destroy   supervision
modify   cheat   obey   purpose   human   illogical
superior   retire   impression   immediately

Example: *Susan was a <u>clever</u> girl.*
You write: *Susan was an intelligent girl.*

1 She was <u>leaving her job</u> because she was 70 years old.

2 The <u>number of people who live</u> in the Solar System is more than 3 billion.

3 He's <u>not playing the game fairly</u>.

4 Robots are more <u>loyal and trustworthy</u> than humans.

5 Robbie always <u>did what</u> Mrs Weston <u>told him to do</u>.

6 Stop this <u>at once</u>.

7 Gloria thought that Robbie was <u>a person</u>.

8 That <u>does not make sense</u>.

9 A simple being cannot create another, more <u>advanced</u> being.

10 Powell and Donovan – you have no <u>reason to be</u> here.

11 That robot is designed to work without <u>people watching it</u>.

12 "<u>Eliminate</u> all sixty-three robots," said the robot-psychologist.

Grammar: syntax

Put the words into the correct order to make sentences.

Example: *A human robot must be harmed to allow a not.*
You write: *A robot must not allow a human to be harmed.*

1 there She was really sure that was not an emergency

2 He's superior humans because he wants that he's to hiding to show

3 I was a candidate that he didn't realize in the election

4 It's the very best humans and a superior robot impossible to tell the difference between

5 Machines who lives, decide It will be the who who, and dies

Published by Macmillan Heinemann ELT
Between Towns Road, Oxford OX4 3PP
A division of Macmillan Publishers Limited
Companies and representatives throughout the world
Heinemann is the registered trademark of Pearson Education, used under licence.

ISBN 978–0–230– 03443–3
ISBN 978–0–230– 02682–7 (with CD pack)

I, Robot by Isaac Asimov copyright Isaac Asimov 1950
This version of *I, Robot* by Isaac Asimov was retold by
Tricia Reilly for Macmillan Readers

First published 2008
Text © Macmillan Publishers Limited 2008
Design and illustration © Macmillan Publishers Limited 2008
This version first published 2008

Illustrated by Simon Williams
Cover by Alamy/I. Glory

Access your audio download at
www.macmillanreaders.com/apefaudio
Password: APEFaudio

Printed and bound in Thailand

2014 2013 2012
10 9 8 7 6

with CD pack
2014 2013 2012
12 11 10 9 8